CW00543064

COLDPLAY

COMPLETE CHORD SONGBOOK

WISE PUBLICATIONS
PART OF THE MUSIC SALES GROUP
LONDON/NEW YORK/PARIS/SYDNEY/COPENHAGEN/BERLIN/MADRID/TOKYO

PUBLISHED BY:
WISE PUBLICATIONS,
14-15 BERNERS STREET, LONDON W1T 3LJ, UK.

EXCLUSIVE DISTRIBUTORS:
MUSIC SALES LIMITED,
DISTRIBUTION CENTRE, NEWMARKET ROAD, BURY ST. EDMUNDS, SUFFOLK IP33 3YB, UK.
MUSIC SALES PTY LIMITED,
20 RESOLUTION DRIVE, CARINGBAH, NSW 2229, AUSTRALIA.

ORDER NO. AM997942
ISBN 978-1-84938-144-4

COMPILED BY NICK CRISPIN.
MUSIC ARRANGED BY MARTIN SHELLARD AND MATT COWE.
MUSIC PROCESSED BY PAUL EWERS MUSIC DESIGN.
PHOTOGRAPH: KEVIN WESTENBERG.
PRINTED IN THE EU.

AY

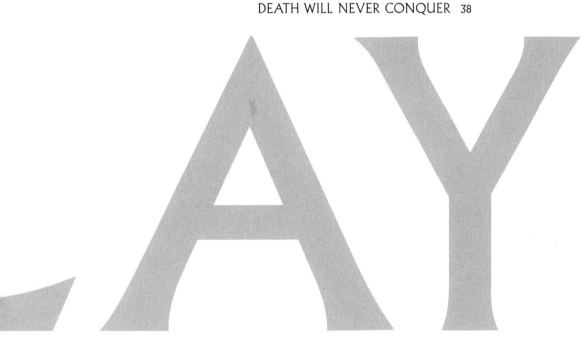

CO

LDP

Relative Tuning

The guitar can be tuned with the aid of pitch pipes or dedicated electronic guitar tuners which are available through your local music dealer. If you do not have a tuning device, you can use relative tuning. Estimate the pitch of the 6th string as near as possible to E or at least a comfortable pitch (not too high, as you might break other strings in tuning up). Then, while checking the various positions on the diagram, place a finger from your left hand on the:

5th fret of the E or 6th string and **tune the open A** (or 5th string) to the note (A)

5th fret of the A or 5th string and **tune the open D** (or 4th string) to the note (D)

5th fret of the D or 4th string and **tune the open G** (or 3rd string) to the note (G)

4th fret of the G or 3rd string and **tune the open B** (or 2nd string) to the note (B)

5th fret of the B or 2nd string and **tune the open E** (or 1st string) to the note (E)

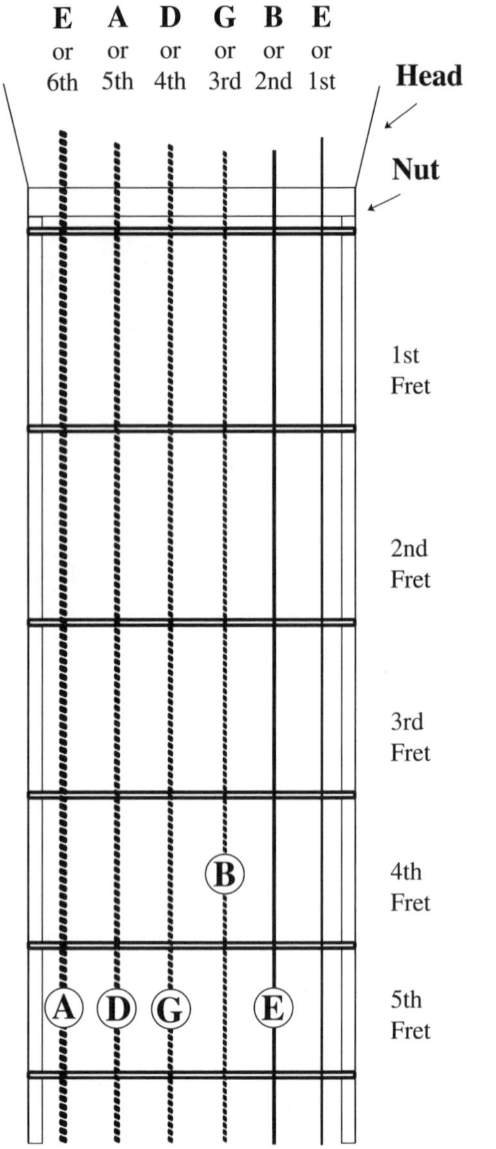

Reading Chord Boxes

Chord boxes are diagrams of the guitar neck viewed head upwards, face on as illustrated. The top horizontal line is the nut, unless a higher fret number is indicated, the others are the frets.

The vertical lines are the strings, starting from E (or 6th) on the left to E (or 1st) on the right.

The black dots indicate where to place your fingers.

Strings marked with an O are played open, not fretted. Strings marked with an X should not be played.

The curved bracket indicates a 'barre' - hold down the strings under the bracket with your first finger, using your other fingers to fret the remaining notes.

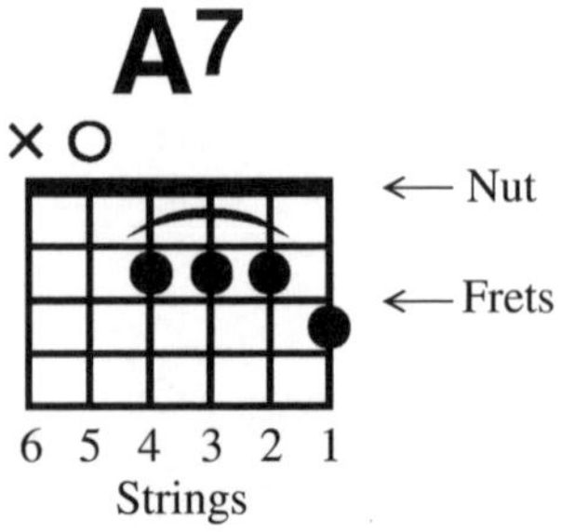

1.36

Words & Music by Guy Berryman, Chris Martin, Jon Buckland & Will Champion

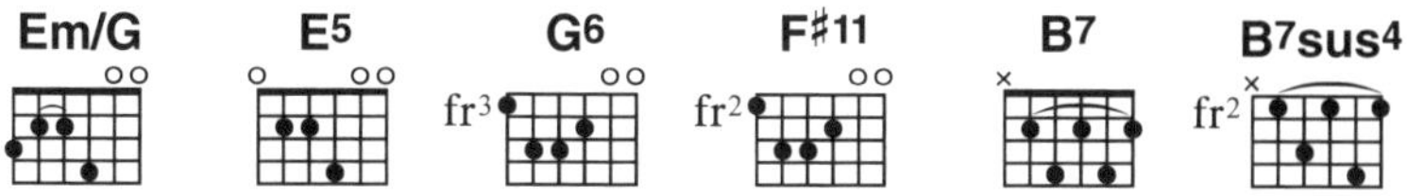

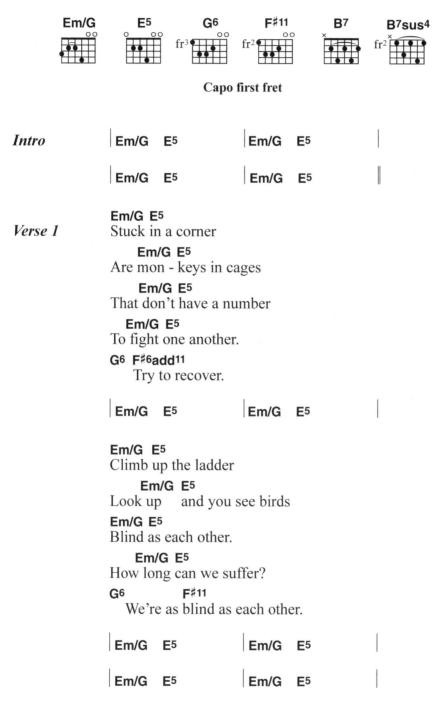

Capo first fret

Intro | Em/G E5 | Em/G E5 |
| Em/G E5 | Em/G E5 ||

Verse 1

Em/G E5
Stuck in a corner

Em/G E5
Are mon - keys in cages

Em/G E5
That don't have a number

Em/G E5
To fight one another.

G6 F♯6add11
Try to recover.

| Em/G E5 | Em/G E5 |

Em/G E5
Climb up the ladder

Em/G E5
Look up and you see birds

Em/G E5
Blind as each other.

Em/G E5
How long can we suffer?

G6 F♯11
We're as blind as each other.

| Em/G E5 | Em/G E5 |
| Em/G E5 | Em/G E5 |

Chorus 1

```
B7          B7sus4
   On the cloud that you sit in
B7                  B7sus4
   There's one born every minute
B7     B7sus4
   So much to discover,
B7       B7sus4
   I've become a believer.

| Em/G   E5        | Em/G   E5         |
| Em/G   E5        | Em/G   E5         |
```

Verse 2

```
Em/G E5
Sis - ters and brothers,
     Em/G E5
Who fight one another
      Em/G  E5
Will mourn and deceive us,
     Em/G E5
Will find  us and keep us.
G6  F#11
   Take us or leave us.

| Em/G   E5        | Em/G   E5         |

Em/G E5
How soon is now? Yeah.
Em/G E5
How long is never?
    Em/G E5
I'm no - thing but normal
       Em/G  E5
With some - thing together.
G6          F#11
   Come on, stick together.

| Em/G   E5        | Em/G   E5         |
| Em/G   E5        | Em/G   E5         |
```

Chorus 2

B7 B7sus4
On the cloud that you sit in

B7 B7sus4
There's one born every minute

B7 B7sus4
So much to discover,

B7 B7sus4
I've become a believer.

Outro

Em/G E5	Em/G E5
Em/G E5	Em/G E5
Em/G E5	Em/G E5
Em/G E5	Em/G E5
G6	F#11 N.C.	

42

Words & Music by Guy Berryman, Chris Martin, Jon Buckland & Will Champion

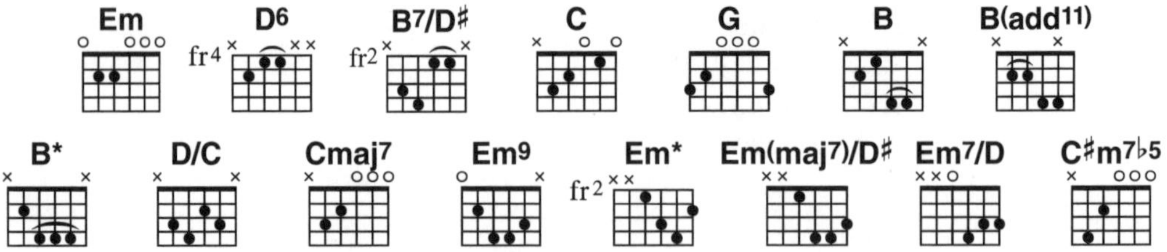

Capo first fret

Verse 1

```
Em
Those who are dead are not dead,
                                    D6        B7/D♯
They're just living in my head.
Em
And since I fell for that spell,
                               D6        B7/D♯
I am living there as well. Oh.
C                                    G
Time is so short and I'm sure
                                        B      B(add11)   B*
There must be something more.
```

Verse 2

```
Em
Those who are dead are not dead,
                                    D6         B7/D♯
They're just living in my head. Oh.
Em
And since I fell for that spell,
                               D6     B7/D♯
I am living there as well. Oh.
C                                    G
Time is so short and I'm sure
                                        B      B(add11)   B*
There must be something more.
C     D/C   Cmaj7   B   Em9
Oh.___________________
```

Double time feel

Interlude 1

| N.C. (E5) | (E5) | (E5) | (E5) |
| (E5) | (E5) | (A5) | (A5) ||

|: (E5) | (E5) | (E5) | (E5) |
| (E5) | (E5) | (A5) | (A5) :|

| (E5) | (E5) | (E5) | (E5) |
| (E5) | (E5) | (A5) | (A5) ||

(A5) (E5)
Ooh, ooh, ooh, ooh.

Ooh, ooh, ooh, ooh.

(A5)
Ooh, ooh, ooh.___

Bridge

G
You thought you might be a ghost,

You thought you might be a ghost.

C
You didn't get to heaven but you made it close,

You didn't get to heaven but you made it close.

G
You thought you might be a ghost,

You thought you might be a ghost.

C
You didn't get to heaven but you made it close,

You didn't get to heaven but you (oh, oh).

Interlude 2

|: G | G | G | G |
| C | C | C | C :|

Half time feel

Outro

Em* Em(maj7)/D#
Those who are dead are not dead,

Em7/D C#m7b5
They're just living in my head. Ooh.___

Amsterdam

Words & Music by Guy Berryman, Chris Martin, Jon Buckland & Will Champion

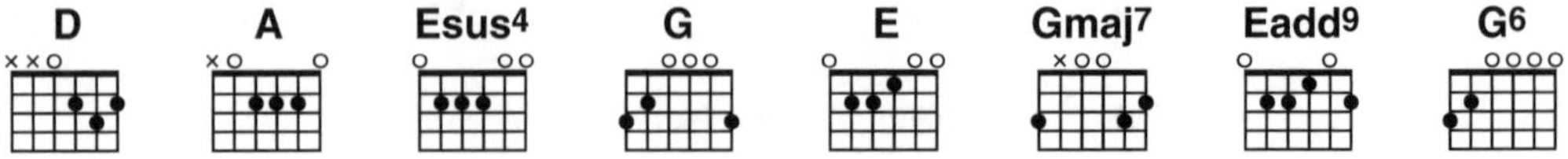

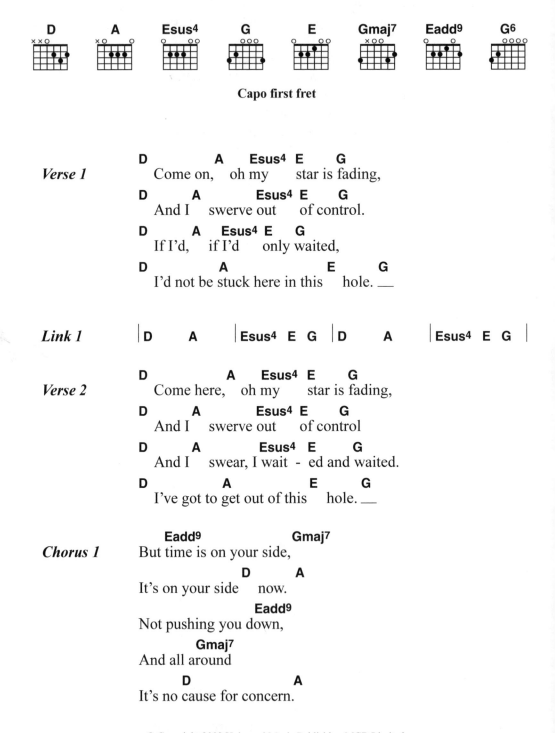

Capo first fret

Verse 1

```
D             A       Esus4  E       G
  Come on,    oh my          star is fading,
D         A              Esus4  E      G
  And I   swerve out            of control.
D         A      Esus4  E      G
  If I'd,   if I'd      only waited,
D                 A                  E          G
  I'd not be stuck here in this      hole. __
```

Link 1

| D A | Esus4 E G | D A | Esus4 E G |

Verse 2

```
D               A       Esus4  E       G
  Come here,    oh my          star is fading,
D         A              Esus4  E      G
  And I   swerve out            of control
D         A               Esus4  E       G
  And I   swear, I wait  -       ed and waited.
D                   A              E          G
  I've got to get out of this      hole. __
```

Chorus 1

```
           Eadd9               Gmaj7
But time is on your side,
                        D         A
It's on your side       now.
                         Eadd9
Not pushing you down,
             Gmaj7
And all around
          D                     A
It's no cause for concern.
```

Instrumental 1 | D A | Esus4 E G | D A | Esus4 E G |

| D A | Esus4 E G | D A | E G ‖

Verse 3

D A Esus4 E G
Come on, oh my star is fading,

D A Esus4 E G
And I see no chance of release.

D A Esus4 E G
And I know I'm dead on the surface

D A Esus4 E Gmaj7
But I am screaming under - neath.__

Chorus 2

Eadd9 Gmaj7
And time is on your side,

D A
It's on your side now.

Eadd9
Not pushing you down,

Gmaj7
And all around

D A
No it's no cause for concern.

Instrumental 2 | Eadd9 | Gmaj7 G6 | D | A |

| Eadd9 | Gmaj7 G6 | D ‖

Chorus 3

A Eadd9 Gmaj7
Stuck on the end of this ball and chain

D A
And I'm on my way back down, yeah.

Eadd9 Gmaj7
Stood on the edge, tied to the noose,

D A
Sick to the stomach.

Eadd9
You can say what you mean,

Gmaj7
But it won't change a thing.

cont.

```
                    D       A
I'm sick of our se - crets.
                      Eadd9                Gmaj7
Stood on the edge,    tied to the noose
                        D                          A      Eadd9
And you came along,    and you cut me loose.
Gmaj7                 D                         A      Eadd9
   You came along    and you cut me loose.
Gmaj7                 D                         A (fermata)
   You came along    and you cut me loose.
```

Animals

Words & Music by Guy Berryman, Chris Martin, Jon Buckland & Will Champion

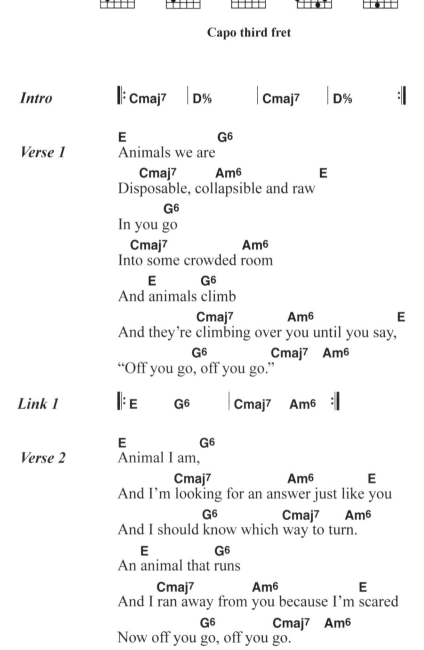

Capo third fret

Intro |: Cmaj7 | D6/9 | Cmaj7 | D6/9 :|

Verse 1

E G6
Animals we are
Cmaj7 Am6 E
Disposable, collapsible and raw
G6
In you go
Cmaj7 Am6
Into some crowded room
E G6
And animals climb
Cmaj7 Am6 E
And they're climbing over you until you say,
G6 Cmaj7 Am6
"Off you go, off you go."

Link 1 |: E G6 | Cmaj7 Am6 :|

Verse 2

E G6
Animal I am,
Cmaj7 Am6 E
And I'm looking for an answer just like you
G6 Cmaj7 Am6
And I should know which way to turn.
E G6
An animal that runs
Cmaj7 Am6 E
And I ran away from you because I'm scared
G6 Cmaj7 Am6
Now off you go, off you go.

```
Chorus 1     Cmaj7                        D6/9
               And if you're gonna go, go now,
             Cmaj7                        D6/9
               And if you're gonna go, go now
             Cmaj7                    D6/9
               And I forgot to tell you how
             Cmaj7                D6/9
               So if you're gonna go… go (now).

Link 2       ||: E      G6      | Cmaj7    Am6  :||
              now.

Verse 3      E          G6
             Animal you are,
                Cmaj7      Am6
             Disposable, defenceless, yes and
             E             G6           Cmaj7       Am6
               Watch your mouth  boys, watch your mouth.
                E          G6
             An animal that runs
                  Cmaj7           Am6
             And I made all my excuses to you
             E                  G6            Cmaj7      Am6
               And I missed my chance by a stone's throw.

Chorus 2     Cmaj7                        D6/9
               And if you're gonna go, go now,
             Cmaj7                        D6/9
               And if you're gonna go, go now
             Cmaj7                    D6/9
               And I forgot to tell you how
             Cmaj7                    D6/9
               So if you're gonna go…   go…

                                                  x4
Link 3       ||: E      G6        | Cmaj7    Am6      :||
              now.                                (go)
```

Outro

```
        E          G6
And I crumble, crumble and fall
Cmaj7                         Am6
Crumble and fall like an animal
  E          G6
I crumble, crumble and fall
Cmaj7                         Am6
Crumble and fall like an animal
       E          G6
Yes I crumble, crumble and fall
Cmaj7                         Am6
Crumble and fall like an animal
       E          G6
Yes I crumble, crumble and fall
Cmaj7                         Am6
Crumble and fall like an animal.

‖: E      G6        | Cmaj7   Am6      :‖
```

Repeat ad lib to finish

Bigger Stronger

Words & Music by Guy Berryman, Chris Martin, Jon Buckland & Will Champion

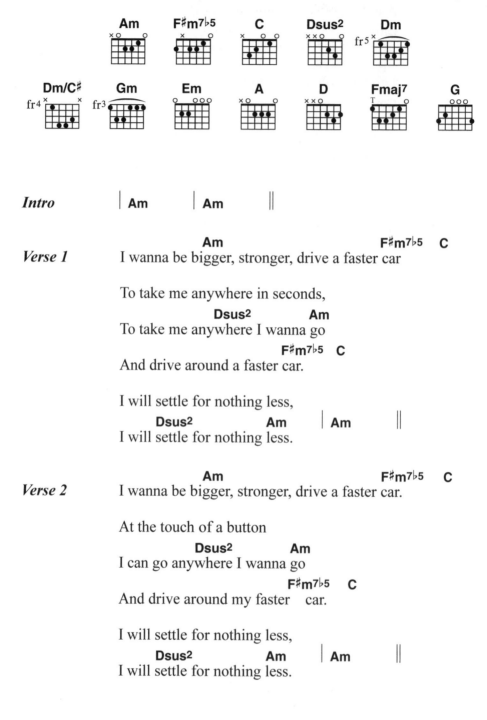

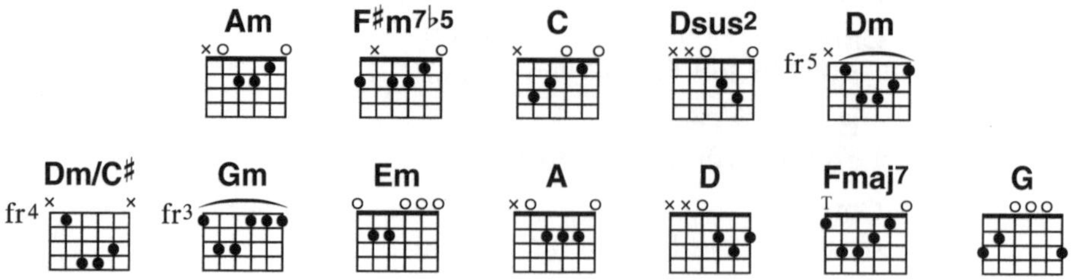

Intro | Am | Am ||

Verse 1

Am F♯m7♭5 C
I wanna be bigger, stronger, drive a faster car

To take me anywhere in seconds,

Dsus2 Am
To take me anywhere I wanna go

F♯m7♭5 C
And drive around a faster car.

I will settle for nothing less,

Dsus2 Am | Am ||
I will settle for nothing less.

Verse 2

Am F♯m7♭5 C
I wanna be bigger, stronger, drive a faster car.

At the touch of a button

Dsus2 Am
I can go anywhere I wanna go

F♯m7♭5 C
And drive around my faster car.

I will settle for nothing less,

Dsus2 Am | Am ||
I will settle for nothing less.

Chorus 1

```
                     Dm       Dm/C♯     Gm
I think I want to change my       altitude,
  C                  Gm      Em      A
I think I want to change my oxygen,
                     Dm          Dm/C♯    Gm    C      Gm
I think I want to change my air,  my   atmosphere,
  Em       A            | A         ||
I want to reach out.
```

Solo 1

```
|: Am      | D        | Am       | D        :|
```

Verse 3

```
                    Am                              F♯m7♭5   C
I wanna be bigger, stronger, drive a faster car

To take me anywhere in seconds,
                      Dsus2            Am
To take me anywhere I wanna go
                                    F♯m7♭5   C
And drive around my faster car.

I will settle for nothing less,
       Dsus2            Am       | Am        ||
I will settle for nothing less.
```

Chorus 2

```
                     Dm      Dm/C♯      Gm
I think I need to change my       altitude,
  C                  Gm      Em      A
I think I want to change my oxygen,
                     Dm          Dm/C♯    Gm    C      Gm
I think I want to change my air, my   atmosphere,
  Em       A           | A      ||
I want to reach out.
```

Solo 2

```
|: Fmaj7   | G   C    | D        | D        :|  Play 4 times

|: Am      | D        | Am       | D        :|
```

Verse 4

```
Am          D       Am          D
Bigger and better, bigger and better,
Am          D       Am          D
Bigger and better, bigger and better,
Am                                F♯m7♭5      C
Bigger, stronger drive a faster car,
                                        Dsus2           Am
At the touch of a button I can go anywhere I wanna go.
```

Brothers And Sisters

Words & Music by Guy Berryman, Chris Martin, Jon Buckland & Will Champion

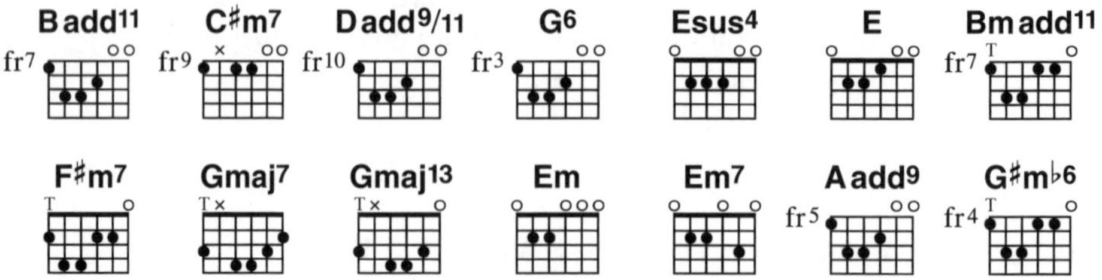

Intro ‖: Badd11 | C#m7 Dadd9/11 | G6 | Esus4 E :‖ *Play 4 time*

Verse 1

Bmadd11 F#m7 Gmaj7
Brothers and sisters unite,
Gmaj13 Bmadd11 F#m7 Gmaj7
It's the time of your lives, it's the time of your lives,
Gmaj13 Bmadd11
Breakdown, break - down,
F#m7 Gmaj7 Em
Got to spread love around, got to spread it around.

Verse 2

Bmadd11 F#m7 Gmaj7
Brothers and sisters feel fine,
Gmaj13 Bmadd11 F#m7 Gmaj7
It's the time of your lives, it's the time of your lives,
Gmaj13 Bmadd11
There's no sound, no sound,
F#m7 Gmaj7 Em
Like this feeling you found, like this feeling you found.

Chorus 1

Badd11 C#m7
But just stay down,
Dadd9/11 C#m7
'Cause sometimes you feel,
Badd11 C#m7
So stay down.

cont.

Dadd9/11 C♯m7 Gmaj7
And sometimes you feel,

Em7 Aadd9 Gmaj7
And it's me they're looking for,

Em7 Aadd9 Gmaj7
And it's me, I will never survive,

Em7 Aadd9
But we'll be around some more.

| Gmaj7 | Gmaj13 | Gmaj7 | Gmaj13 ||

Verse 3

Bmadd11 F♯m7 Gmaj7
Brothers and sisters unite,

Gmaj13 Bmadd11 F♯m7 Gmaj7
It's the time of your lives, it's the time of your lives,

Gmaj13 Bmadd11
Breakdown, break - down,

F♯m7 Gmaj7 Em
Got to spread love around, got to spread it all round.

Chorus 2

Badd11 C♯m7
But just stay down,

Dadd9/11 C♯m7
And sometimes you'll feel,

Badd11 C♯m7
So stay around.

Dadd9/11 C♯m7 Gmaj7
And sometimes you'll feel,

Em7 Aadd9 Gmaj7
And it's me they're looking for,

Em7 Aadd9 Gmaj7
And it's me, I will never survive,

Em7 Aadd9
But we'll be around some more.

| Gmaj7 | Gmaj13 | Gmaj7 | Gmaj13 ||

Outro

| Badd11 | C♯m7 Dadd9/11 | G6 | Esus4 E |
It's gonna be al -

| Badd11 | Badd11 G♯m♭6 | F♯m7 | E |
- right. It's gonna be al -

| Badd11 | C♯m7 Dadd9/11 | G6 | F♯m7 |
- right. It's gonna be al -

| Badd11 | C♯m7 Dadd9/11 | G6 | F♯m7 ||
- right.

Careful Where You Stand

Words & Music by Guy Berryman, Chris Martin, Jon Buckland & Will Champion

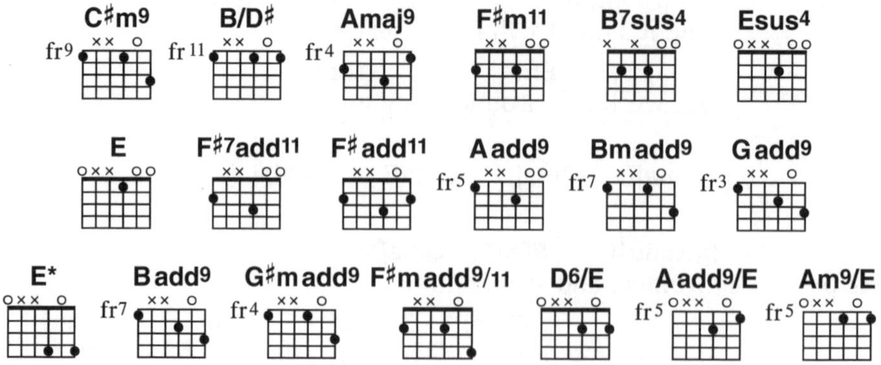

Intro ‖: C♯m9 | C♯m9 B/D♯ | C♯m9 | C♯m9 B/D♯ :‖

Verse 1

C♯m9 B/D♯ C♯m9 B/D♯
I feel safe, I feel warm
C♯m9 B/D♯ C♯m9
When you're here, can I do no wrong?
Amaj9 F♯m11 C♯m9
I am cured when I'm by your side,
B7sus4 Esus4 E
I'm alright, I'm alright.

Verse 2

C♯m9 B/D♯ C♯m9
I am safe when I am with you,
B/D♯ C♯m9 B/D♯ C♯m9
And I feel warm, if you want me to.
Amaj9 F♯m11 C♯m9
I am cured when I'm by your side,
F♯7add11 F♯add11
I'm alright.

| F♯7add11 F♯add11 | Aadd9 Amaj9 | Aadd9 ‖

Chorus 1

Bmadd9 Gadd9 E* Gadd9
Careful where you stand, my love,
Bmadd9 Gadd9 E* Gadd9
Careful where you lay your head.

```
              Badd9   G#madd9     Gadd9
cont.         It's true, _______ we're always there
                        F#madd9/11   D6/E   | E*    | D6/E  | E*    ||
              Looking out for one another.

                  C#m9          B/D#   C#m9
Verse 3       I feel   safe when I am   with you,
                B/D#   C#m9                    B/D#    C#m9
              And I     feel warm, when you want me to.
                 Amaj9  F#m11                 C#m9
              I am cured     when you're all alone,
                 F#7add11   F#add11
              I'm alright.

              | Aadd9  Amaj9  | Aadd9     ||

              Bmadd9              Gadd9     E*     Gadd9
Chorus 2      Careful where you stand, my love,
              Bmadd9              Gadd9   E*     Gadd9
              Careful where you lay your head.
                 Badd9   G#madd9     Gadd9
              It's true, _______ we're always
                        F#madd9/11   E*
              Looking out for one another.

Link 1        | Aadd9/E | Am9/E  | E*     | Aadd9/E | Am9/E  | E*     ||

                 Aadd9/E   Am9/E       E*
Bridge 1      So I'd like a   quiet town, please,
                    Aadd9/E   Am9/E         Bmadd9 | Gadd9 | E*    | Gadd9 ||
              Yeah, I'd like a   quiet town. _____

Link 2        | Bmadd9 | Gadd9 | E*     | Gadd9 ||

              Bmadd9     Gadd9         E*           Gadd9
Bridge 2      Ooh now, _______ now, ______ ooh. ______
              Bmadd9     Gadd9         E*           Gadd9
              Ooh now, _______ now, ______ ooh. ______
                  Badd9   G#madd9  Gadd9   F#madd9/11
              And care - ful where  you     stand,
                  Badd9   G#madd9  Gadd9   F#madd9/11
              And care - ful where  you     stand. ____

              | Badd9   | G#madd9 | Gadd9  | Gadd9  ||
```

Cemeteries Of London

Words & Music by Guy Berryman, Chris Martin, Jon Buckland & Will Champion

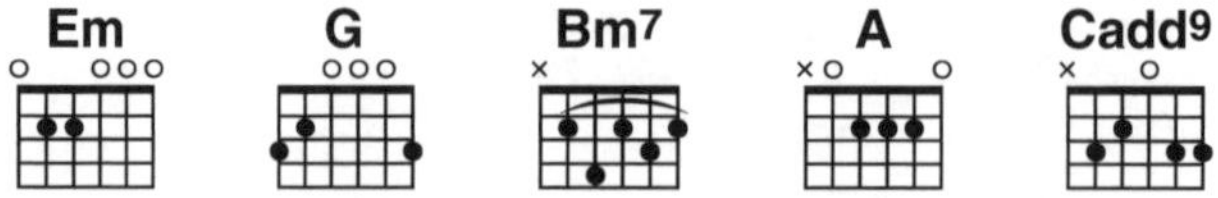

Tune guitar down a semitone

Verse 1

Em
At night they would go walking

Till the breaking of the day,

The morning is for sleeping.

Through the dark streets they go searching

To see God in their own way,

Save the night time for your weeping,

Your weeping.

Chorus 1

G A Em
Singing la, la, la, la, la, la, la, lay.
C(add9) Bm7 Em
And the night over London lay.

Verse 2

Em G
So we rode down to the river,
Bm7 Em
Where Vic - torian ghosts pray
G Bm7
For their curses to be broken.
Em G
We go underneath the arches
Bm7 Em
Where the witches are, and they say
G Bm7
There are ghost towns in the ocean,
Em
The ocean.

Chorus 2

```
       G       A             Em
Singing la, la, la, la, la, la, la, lay.
            C(add9)   Bm7      Em
And the night over London lay.
```

Instr.

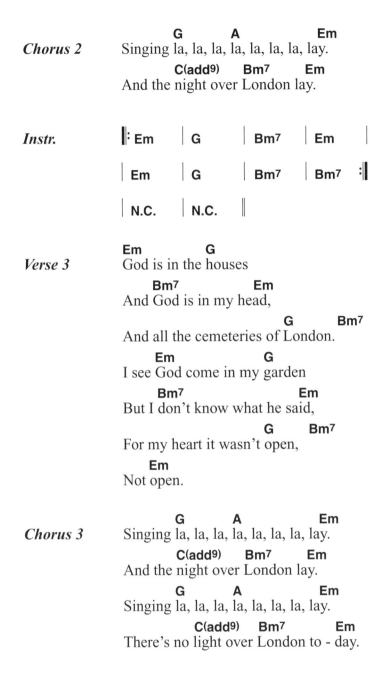

```
|: Em  | G   | Bm7 | Em  |
|  Em  | G   | Bm7 | Bm7 :|
|  N.C.| N.C.||
```

Verse 3

```
Em          G
God is in the houses
     Bm7           Em
And God is in my head,
                            G       Bm7
And all the cemeteries of London.
     Em              G
I see God come in my garden
     Bm7                  Em
But I don't know what he said,
                       G      Bm7
For my heart it wasn't open,
   Em
Not open.
```

Chorus 3

```
       G       A             Em
Singing la, la, la, la, la, la, la, lay.
            C(add9)   Bm7      Em
And the night over London lay.
       G       A             Em
Singing la, la, la, la, la, la, la, lay.
               C(add9)   Bm7         Em
There's no light over London to - day.
```

Chinese Sleep Chant

Words & Music by Guy Berryman, Chris Martin, Jon Buckland & Will Champion

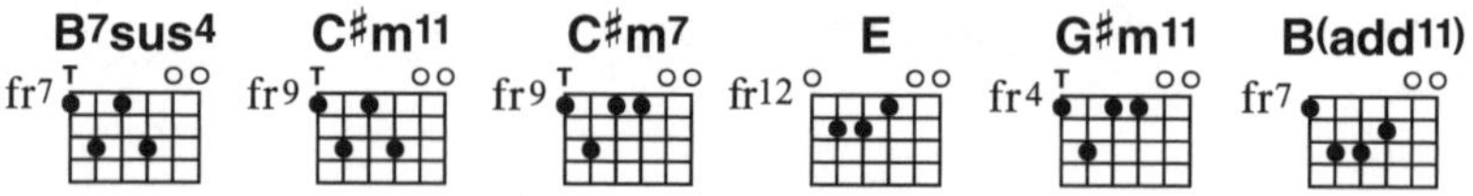

Intro ‖: B7sus4 | B7sus4 | B7sus4 | B7sus4 |
| C#m11 | C#m7 | C#m11 | C#m7 :‖

Verse 1

B7sus4
Ah, sleep, I need.
C#m11 C#m7 C#m11 C#m7
Sleep sa - tisfies, sleep sa - tisfies.
B7sus4
Ah, sleep, I need.
C#m11 C#m7 C#m11 C#m7
Sleep sa - tisfies, sleep sa - tisfies.

Chorus 1

E C#m11 C#m7 C#m11 C#m7
Sleep, sleep, sleep.
E
Sleep, sleep.
C#m11 C#m7 C#m11 C#m7
Sleep sa - tisfies, sleep sa - tisfies.

Verse 2

B7sus4
Fall asleep, fall asleep.
C#m11 C#m7 C#m11 C#m7
Sleep mys - tifies, sleep mys - tifies.
B7sus4
Fall asleep , fall asleep.
C#m11 C#m7 C#m11 C#m7
Sleep sa - tisfies, sleep sa - tisfies.

Guitar solo

| E | E | E | E |

| C♯m7 | C♯m7 E | G♯m11 | G♯m11 B(add11) |

| E | E | E | E |

| C♯m7 | C♯m7 E | G♯m11 | G♯m11 B(add11) ||

Chorus 2

```
E                  C♯m11  C♯m7  C♯m11  C♯m7
   Sleep, sleep, sleep.
E
   Sleep, sleep.
C♯m11      C♯m7   C♯m11     C♯m7    E
Sleep sa - tisfies, sleep sa - tisfies.
```

Clocks

Words & Music by Guy Berryman, Chris Martin, Jon Buckland & Will Champion

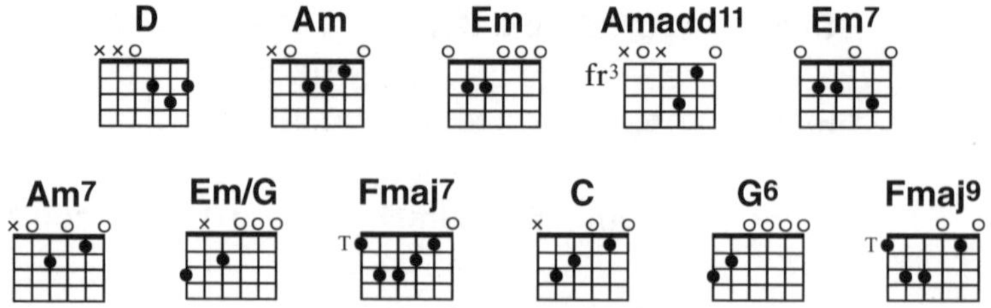

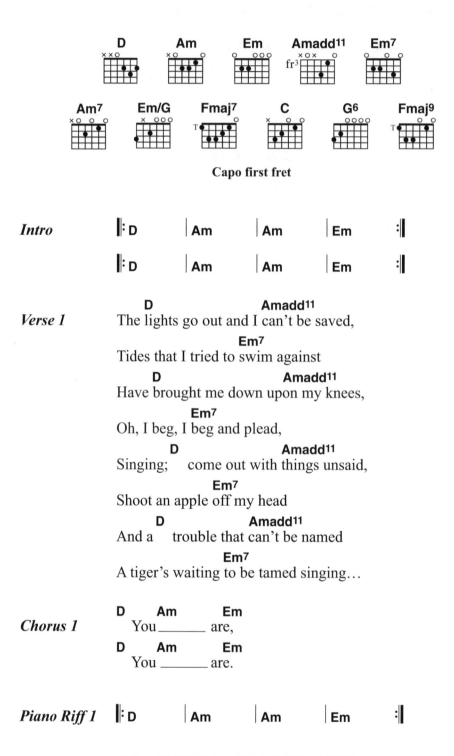

Capo first fret

Intro ‖: D | Am | Am | Em :‖

‖: D | Am | Am | Em :‖

Verse 1

```
        D                     Amadd11
The lights go out and I can't be saved,
                        Em7
Tides that I tried to swim against
       D                       Amadd11
Have brought me down upon my knees,
              Em7
Oh, I beg, I beg and plead,
           D                    Amadd11
Singing;    come out with things unsaid,
                  Em7
Shoot an apple off my head
        D                Amadd11
And a    trouble that can't be named
                    Em7
A tiger's waiting to be tamed singing…
```

Chorus 1

```
D      Am         Em
  You_______  are,
D      Am         Em
  You _______ are.
```

Piano Riff 1 ‖: D | Am | Am | Em :‖

Verse 2

```
D                   Amadd11
Confusion that never stops,
                          Em7
The closing walls and ticking clocks
        D                    Amadd11
Gonna   come back and take you home
                        Em7
I could not stop that you now know,
          D            Amadd11
Singing;  come out upon my seas,
                          Em7
Cursed missed opportunities
      D        Amadd11
Am I  a part of the cure,
                   Em7
Or am I part of the disease?  Singing…
```

Chorus 2

```
D      Am       Em
  You _____ are,
D      Am       Em
  You _____ are.
D      Am       Em
  You _____ are,
D      Am       Em
  You _____ are.
```

Instrumental

```
                                       x3
|: D       | Am7     | Am7     | Em/G     :|
```

```
D      Am7      Em/G
  You _____ are.
```

Bridge

```
Fmaj7                C         G6
  And nothing else compares
Fmaj7                  C         G6
  Oh no nothing else compares,
Fmaj7                C         G6    Fmaj7   Fmaj9   Fmaj7   Fmaj9
  And nothing else compares.
```

Piano riff 2

```
|: D       | Am      | Am      | Em       :|

|: D       | Am7     | Am7     | Em/G     :|
```

Chorus 3

```
D        Am7        Em/G
  You ——— are,
D        Am7        Em/G
  You ——— are.
```

Outro

```
    D          Am7                      Em/G
‖: Home, home, where I wanted to go.
D            Am7                      Em/G
Home, home, where I wanted to go.  :‖
```

Repeat to fade

Crests Of Waves

Words & Music by Guy Berryman, Chris Martin, Jon Buckland & Will Champion

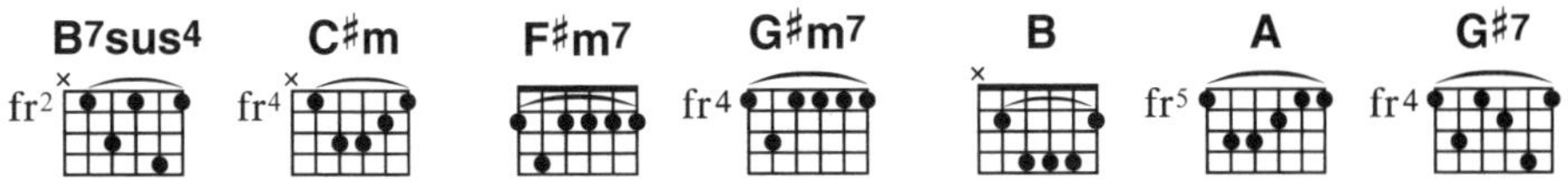

Intro

| B7sus4 |

| C#m | F#m7 G#m7 | C#m | F#m7 G#m7 |

| C#m | F#m7 G#m7 | F#m7 | G#m7 B |

Verse 1

                 C#m   A
It could be worse, I could be alone
               F#m7   G#m7
I could be locked in here on my own
            C#m   A
Or like a stone that certainly drops
           F#m7 G#m7
It never stops, no.
B   C#m   A
I could be lost, or I could be saved
          F#m7   G#m7
Calling out from beneath the waves
          C#m   A
Beaten down by the sloshing rain
          F#m7   G#m7   B
Never again, never again.

Chorus 1

C#m   F#m7   G#m7
Oo   -   oo   -   oo
C#m   F#m7   G#m7
Oo   -   oo   -   oo
C#m   F#m7   G#m7
Oo   -   oo   -   oo
           F#m7   G#m7
Skating out from the crests of waves.

Link 1

| C#m | F#m7 G#m7 | C#m | F#m7 G#m7 |

| C#m | F#m7 G#m7 | F#m7 | G#m7 B |

```
                    C♯m                A
Verse 2      It could be worse, it's all sweet
                        F♯m7                          G♯m7
             You could be snapped from the jaws of defeat.
                   C♯m7                   A
             Or like a light lit up on a beach
                                      F♯m7   G♯m7
             Wear your heart on your sleeve, oh.
             B              C♯m                 A
             You want to stop before you begin
                          F♯m7                             G♯m7
             You want to sink when you know you could swim.
                          C♯m                    A
             You want to stop just before you begin
                         F♯m7         G♯m7    B
             Never give in, never give in.

             C♯m       F♯m7      G♯m7
Chorus 2     Oo    -   oo    -   oo
             C♯m       F♯m7      G♯m7
             Oo    -   oo    -   oo
             C♯m       F♯m7      G♯m7
             Oo    -   oo    -   oo
                     F♯m7                    G♯m7
             Skating out from the crests of waves.

             A
Bridge          Nothing matters,
             F♯m7      G♯m7
                Except life and the love we make
             A
                Nothing matters
             F♯m7      G♯m7
                Except life and the love we make
             A
                Nothing matters
             F♯m7      G♯m7
                Except life and the love we make
             F♯m7      G♯m7
                                  Except life and the love we make.
```

Chorus 3

```
C#m         F#m7     G#m7
Oo    -     oo   -   oo
C#m         F#m7     G#m7
Oo    -     oo   -   oo
C#m         F#m7     G#m7
Oo    -     oo   -   oo
        F#m7                  G#m7
Skating out from the crests of waves.
C#m         F#m7     G#m7
Oo    -     oo   -   oo
C#m         F#m7     G#m7
Oo    -     oo   -   oo
C#m         F#m7     G#m7
Oo    -     oo   -   oo
        F#m7                  G#m7
Skating out from the crests of waves.
        F#m7         G#m7
You're longing to be saved,
           F#m7                  G#m7
Screaming out from the crests of waves,
        F#m7         G#m7
You're longing to be saved,
           F#m7                  G#m7
Screaming out from the crests of waves.
```

Daylight

Words & Music by Guy Berryman, Chris Martin, Jon Buckland & Will Champion

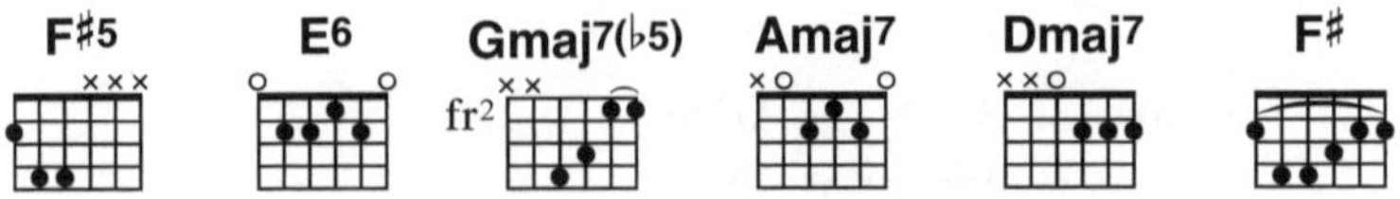

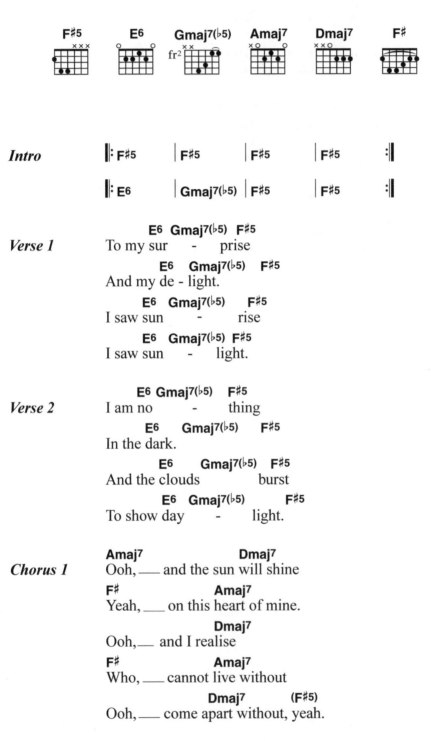

Intro ‖: F♯5 | F♯5 | F♯5 | F♯5 :‖

‖: E6 | Gmaj7(♭5) | F♯5 | F♯5 :‖

Verse 1

E6 Gmaj7(♭5) F♯5
To my sur - prise
E6 Gmaj7(♭5) F♯5
And my de - light.
E6 Gmaj7(♭5) F♯5
I saw sun - rise
E6 Gmaj7(♭5) F♯5
I saw sun - light.

Verse 2

E6 Gmaj7(♭5) F♯5
I am no - thing
E6 Gmaj7(♭5) F♯5
In the dark.
E6 Gmaj7(♭5) F♯5
And the clouds burst
E6 Gmaj7(♭5) F♯5
To show day - light.

Chorus 1

Amaj7 Dmaj7
Ooh,__ and the sun will shine
F♯ Amaj7
Yeah,__ on this heart of mine.
Dmaj7
Ooh,__ and I realise
F♯ Amaj7
Who,__ cannot live without
Dmaj7 (F♯5)
Ooh,__ come apart without, yeah.

Link 1

| F♯5 | F♯5 | F♯5 | F♯5 |

||: E6 | Gmaj7(♭5) | F♯5 | F♯5 :||

Verse 3

E6 Gmaj7(♭5) F♯5
On a hill - top
E6 Gmaj7(♭5) F♯5
On a sky rise.
E6 Gmaj7(♭5) F♯5 E6 Gmaj7(♭5) F♯5
Like a first born child.

Verse 4

E6 Gmaj7(♭5) F♯5
On a full tilt,
E6 Gmaj7(♭5) F♯5
And in full flight
E6 Gmaj7(♭5) F♯5
Defeat dark - ness
E6 Gmaj7(♭5) F♯5
Breaking day - light.

Chorus 2

Amaj7 Dmaj7
Ooh,___ and the sun will shine
F♯ Amaj7
Yeah,___ on this heart of mine.
Dmaj7
Ooh,___ and I realise
F♯ Amaj7
Who,___ cannot live without
Amaj7 Dmaj7 F♯5 | F♯5 | F♯5 | F♯5 ||
Ooh,___ come apart without, daylight.

Outro

E6 Gmaj7(♭5)
||: Slowly breaking through the daylight,
F♯5
Slowly breaking through the daylight. :|| *Repeat to fade*

Death And All His Friends

Words & Music by Guy Berryman, Chris Martin, Jon Buckland & Will Champion

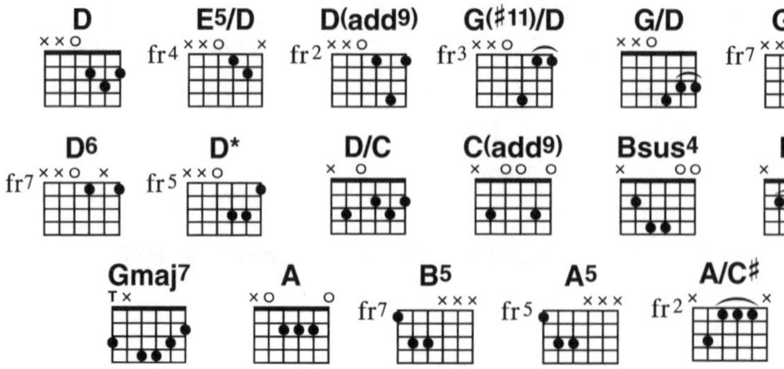

Capo first fret

Verse 1

```
D   E5/D  D   D(add9)  G♯11/D   G/D
All win - ter we got    car   -  ried
    G/D*  D6   D*           C/D        C(add9)      Bsus4  Bm
A - way   o  -  ver on the rooftops,       let's get mar  -  ried.
D   E5/D  D     D(add9)  G♯11/D   G/D
All sum - mer we just    hur   -  ried,
G/D*      D6   D*             C/D          C(add9)   Bsus4  Bm
So come o  -  ver just be patient and        don't wor  -  ry.
G/D*      D6   D*             C/D          C(add9)   Bsus4  Bm
So come o  -  ver just be patient and        don't wor  -  ry.
```

Instr.

```
|: D          E5/D  | D        D(add9)  |
|  G♯11/D           | G/D   G/D*   D6   |
|  D*         D/C   | D/C   C(add9)     |
|  Bsus4            | Bm             :|
```

Verse 2

```
G/D*      D6   D*             C/D          C(add9)   Bsus4  Bm   Gmaj7
So come o  -  ver just be patient and        don't wor  -  ry.

And don't worry.
```

Bridge

| D | D | D | D |

| D | D | D6 | D6 |

| D | D | D | D |
Try.

| D | D | D6 | D6 |
Try.

| B5 | A5 |

| D | D | D | D |

| D | D | D6 | D6 |
Try.

| B5 | A5 |

| D | D | D6 | D A ||
Try.

Interlude

||: Gmaj7 Bm | A Bm A/C# |

| D A | Gmaj7 Bm A :||

Chorus

(Bm) (A) Gmaj7 Bm
No I don't want to battle from beginning to end,
A Bm
I don't want a cycle of recycled revenge,
A/C# D A Gmaj7
I don't want to follow death and all of his friends.
Bm A Gmaj7 Bm
No I don't want to battle from beginning to end,
A Bm
I don't want a cycle of recycled revenge,
A/C# D A
I don't want to follow death and all of his friends.

Outro

| Gmaj7 Bm A | Gmaj7 Bm A | Gmaj7 Bm A |

| Gmaj7 Bm A | Gmaj7 Bm A | Gmaj7 ||

Death Will Never Conquer

Words & Music by Guy Berryman, Chris Martin, Jon Buckland & Will Champion

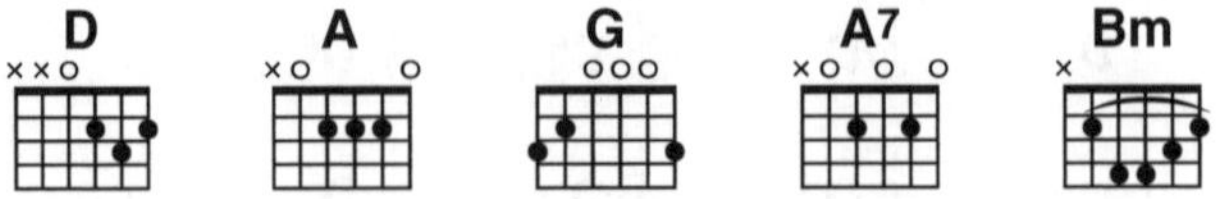

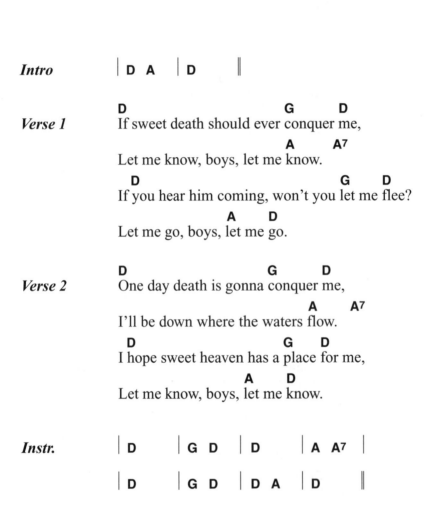

Capo first fret

Intro | D A | D ||

Verse 1

```
D                                G         D
If sweet death should ever conquer me,
                                 A         A7
Let me know, boys, let me know.
  D                                      G       D
If you hear him coming, won't you let me flee?
                    A       D
Let me go, boys, let me go.
```

Verse 2

```
D                            G         D
One day death is gonna conquer me,
                                  A        A7
I'll be down where the waters flow.
 D                               G       D
I hope sweet heaven has a place for me,
                        A       D
Let me know, boys, let me know.
```

Instr. | D | G D | D | A A7 |
| D | G D | D A | D ||

Verse 3

```
D                          G       D
If sweet death should ever conquer me,
                                A      A7
Take me down to some place be - low.
   D                                 G     D
If you hear him coming won’t you set me free?
                 A      D
Let me go, boys, let me go.
   Bm           A                 G        D
If you hear him coming, won’t you sing for me?
                  A       D
That I just don’t want to go.
```

Don't Panic

Words & Music by Guy Berryman, Chris Martin, Jon Buckland & Will Champion

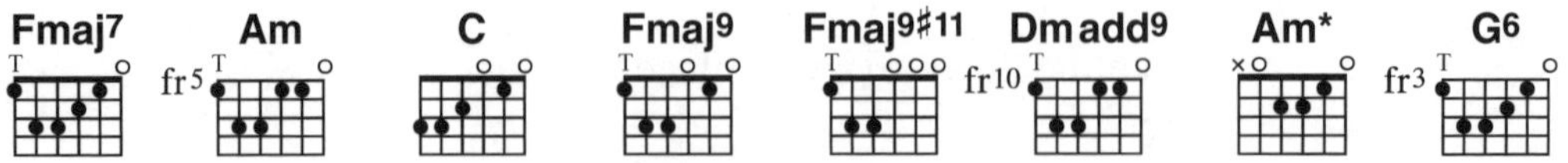

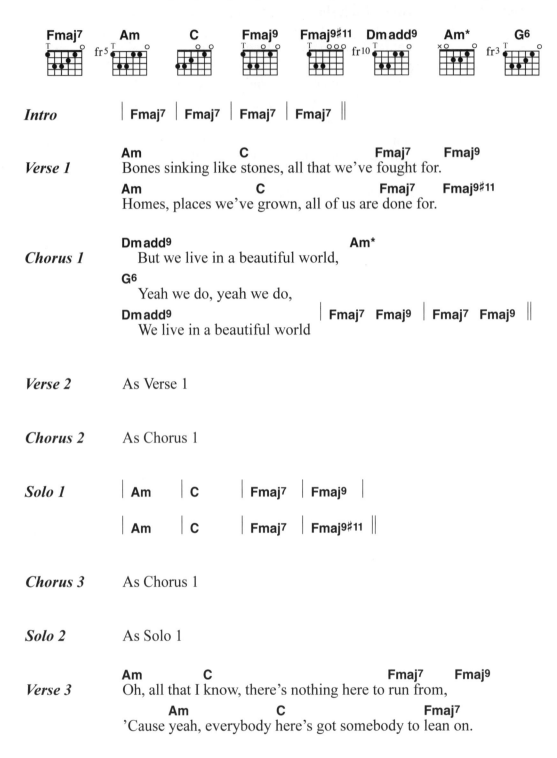

Intro | Fmaj7 | Fmaj7 | Fmaj7 | Fmaj7 ||

Verse 1
Am C Fmaj7 Fmaj9
Bones sinking like stones, all that we've fought for.
Am C Fmaj7 Fmaj9♯11
Homes, places we've grown, all of us are done for.

Chorus 1
Dmadd9 Am*
But we live in a beautiful world,
G6
Yeah we do, yeah we do,
Dmadd9 | Fmaj7 Fmaj9 | Fmaj7 Fmaj9 ||
We live in a beautiful world

Verse 2 As Verse 1

Chorus 2 As Chorus 1

Solo 1 | Am | C | Fmaj7 | Fmaj9 |
| Am | C | Fmaj7 | Fmaj9♯11 ||

Chorus 3 As Chorus 1

Solo 2 As Solo 1

Verse 3
Am C Fmaj7 Fmaj9
Oh, all that I know, there's nothing here to run from,
Am C Fmaj7
'Cause yeah, everybody here's got somebody to lean on.

Glass Of Water

Words & Music by Guy Berryman, Chris Martin, Jon Buckland & Will Champion

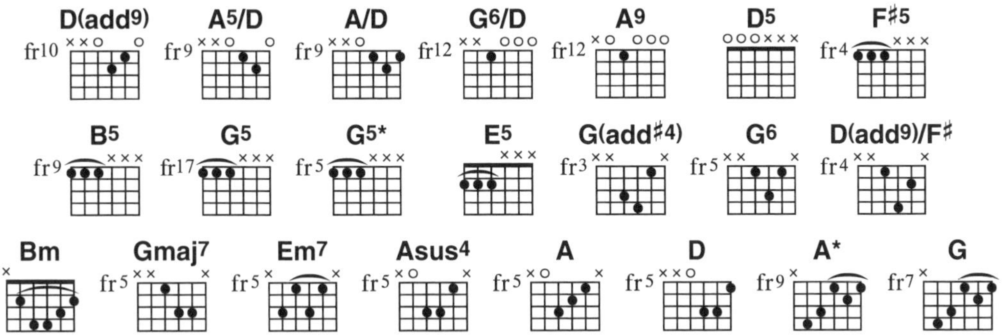

Tune sixth string to D

Verse 1

D(add9)   A5/D   A/D   D(add9)
Scared of losing all the time,
  A5/D   A/D D(add9)
He wrote it in a letter,
  A5/D A/D   D(add9) A5/D A/D
He was a friend of mine.
D(add9) A5/D   A/D   D(add9)
He heard you could see your future
  A5/D A/D   D(add9)
In - side a glass of water,
  A5/D A/D   D(add9) A5/D A/D
The ripples and the lines.
  G6/D   A9
And he asked, "Will I see heaven in mine?"

Link 1

| D(add9) | A5/D A/D | D(add9) | A5/D A/D ||

Verse 2

```
D(add9) A5/D    A/D    D(add9)
That is  just the way it was,
A5/D      A/D        D(add9)
Nothing could be better,
      A5/D     A/D  D(add9)    A5/D   A/D
And nothing ever was.
    D(add9)  A5/D     A/D       D(add9)
Oh they say you can see your future
     A5/D  A/D       D(add9)
In - side a glass of water,
     A5/D    A/D      D(add9)    A5/D   A/D
The riddles and the rhymes.
G6/D                              A9
   Will I see heaven in mine? Oh, I...
```

Chorus 1

```
D5     F#5  B5   G5
Son,
       D5    F#5   B5
Don't ask,
G5           D5      F#5  B5      G5          D5       F#5   B5   G5
   Neither half full or empty     is your glass.
D5       F#5   B5   G5
Cling,
        D5      F#5   B5   G5
To the mast,
G5                 D5        F#5   B5      G5          G5*     E5
   Spend your whole life     living     in the past,
G5*         E5
   Going nowhere fast.
```

Link 2

```
|: D(add9)   | A5/D   A/D | D(add9)   | A5/D   A/D :|
```

Verse 3

```
D(add9) A5/D      A/D  D(add9)
So he    wrote it on a wall,
     A5/D       A/D   D(add9)
The hollow - est of halos
   A5/D A/D      D(add9)  A5/D   A/D
Is no    halo at all.
D(add9)  A5/D   A/D
Tele   -   vision selling
D(add9)  A5/D  A/D       D(add9)
Plastic   figu - rines of leaders
      A5/D        A/D    D(add9)      A5/D   A/D
Say - ing noth - ing at all.
                  G6/D                         A9
And we chime,     "Stars in heaven align." Oh, I...
```

Chorus 2

```
D5    F♯5   B5   G5
Son,
         D5    F♯5   B5
Don't ask,
G5            D5       F♯5  B5       G5            D5        F♯5   B5   G5
   Neither half full or empty      is your glass.
D5       F♯5   B5   G5
Cling,
          D5       F♯5   B5   G5
To the mast,
G5                 D5        F♯5   B5      G5          G5*     E5
   Spend your whole life      living     in the past,
G5*         E5
   Going nowhere fast.
```

Interlude

```
| G(add♯4)    | G(add♯4)    | G6    | G6    |
| D(add9)/F♯  | D(add9)/F♯  | Bm    | Bm    |
| Gmaj7       | Gmaj7       | Em7   | Em7   |
| Asus4       | Asus4       | A     | A     ||
||: D5  F♯5   | B5  G5      | D5  F♯5 | B5  G5 :||
| D5          ||
```

Outro

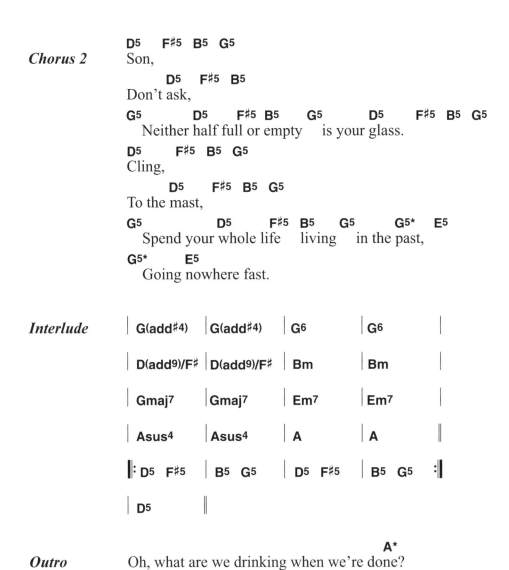

```
                                                  A*
Oh, what are we drinking when we're done?
                 G         D
Glasses of water.
```

Easy To Please

Words & Music by Guy Berryman, Chris Martin, Jon Buckland & Will Champion

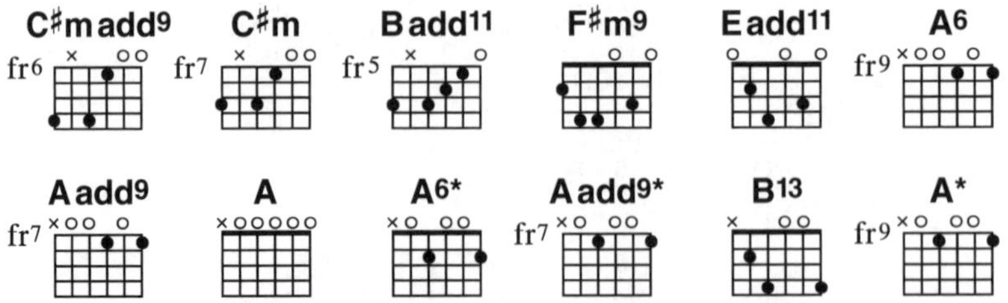

Tune guitar (from bottom string): D, G, D, G, B, D, then Capo second fret

Intro | C♯madd9 | C♯madd9 ||

Verse 1

C♯m Badd11
Love, I hope we get old,
F♯m9 Eadd11
I hope we can find a way of seeing it all.
C♯m Badd11
Love, I hope we can be,
F♯m9
I hope I can find a way
A6 Aadd9 A6 Aadd9
Of letting you see
A A6* Aadd9* A6* A
That I'm so ea - - sy to please,
A6* Aadd9* A6*
So ea - - - (sy.)

| B13 Aadd9* A* | B13 Aadd9* A* |
- - sy.

| B13 Aadd9* A* | B13 Aadd9* A* ||

Verse 2

C♯m Badd11
Love, I hope we grow old,

F♯m9 Eadd11
I hope we can find a way of seeing it all.

C♯m Badd11
Love, I hope we can be,

F♯m9
I hope I can find a way

A6 Aadd9 A6 Aadd9
Of letting you see

A A6* Aadd9* A6* A
That I'm so ea - - sy to please,

A6* Aadd9* A6*
So ea - - - (sy.)

| B13 Aadd9* A* | B13 Aadd9* A* |
- - sy.

| B13 Aadd9* A* | B13 Aadd9* A* ||

The Escapist

Words & Music by Guy Berryman, Chris Martin, Jon Buckland, Will Champion & Jon Hopkins

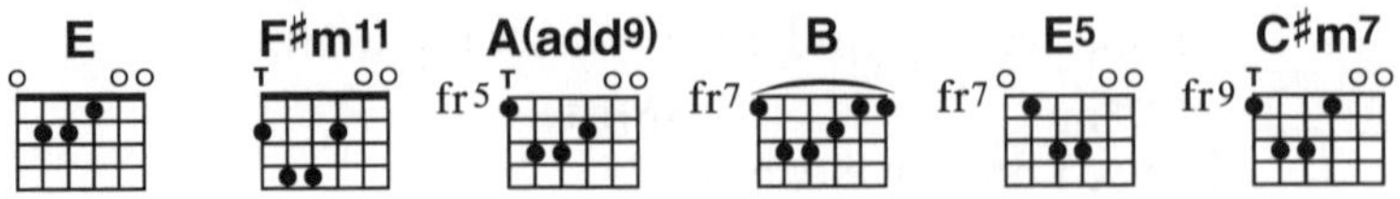

Intro

N.C.	E	F♯m11 A(add9)	A(add9) B
E5 C♯m7	F♯m11 A(add9)	A(add9) B
B C♯m7	F♯m11 A(add9)	A(add9) B
E5 C♯m7	F♯m11 A(add9)	A(add9) B
B C♯m7	F♯m11 A(add9)	A(add9) B
E5 C♯m7	

Verse

F♯m11 A(add9) B C♯m7 F♯m11 A(add9)
And in the end we lie a - wake,
B E5 C♯m7
And we dream we'll make an escape.
F♯m11 A(add9) B C♯m7 F♯m11 A(add9)
And in the end we lie a - wake,
B E C♯m7
And we dream we'll make an escape.

Outro

| F♯m11 A(add9) | A(add9) B | B C♯m7 |
Ooh.________________________ Ooh.__

| F♯m11 A(add9) | A(add9) B | E C♯m7 |
______________ Ooh.__________

| F♯m11 A(add9) | A(add9) B | B C♯m7 |
____________________ Ooh.__________

| F♯m11 A(add9) | A(add9) B | E C♯m7 |
______________ *cont. ad lib. sim.*

| F♯m11 A(add9) | A(add9) B | B C♯m7 |

| F♯m11 A(add9) | A(add9) B | E C♯m7 |

| F♯m11 A(add9) | A(add9) B | B C♯m7 |

| F♯m11 A(add9) | N.C. | N.C. | N.C. | N.C. |
Ooh.______________ Ooh.________

| N.C. | N.C. ‖ *Fade out*

Everything's Not Lost

Words & Music by Guy Berryman, Chris Martin, Jon Buckland & Will Champion

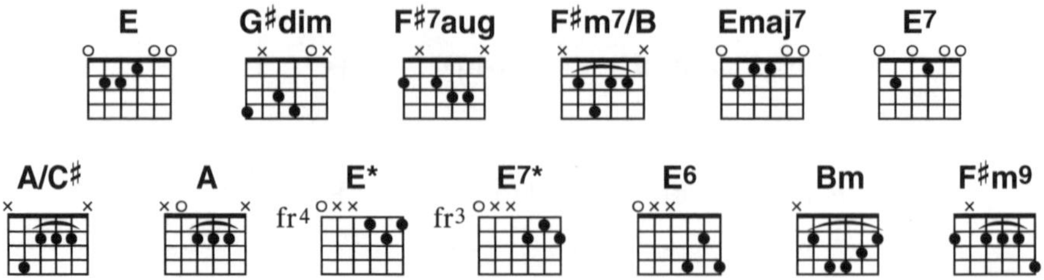

Verse 1

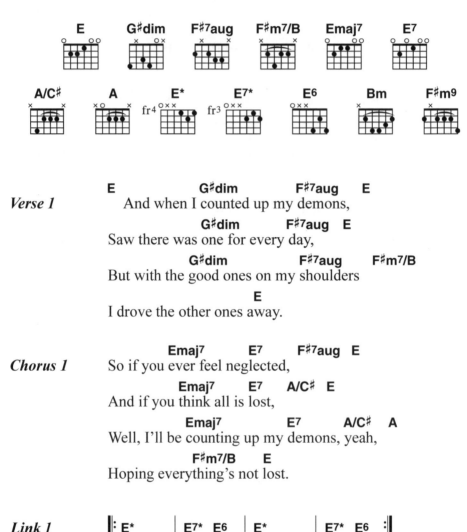

E G♯dim F♯7aug E
And when I counted up my demons,
G♯dim F♯7aug E
Saw there was one for every day,
G♯dim F♯7aug F♯m7/B
But with the good ones on my shoulders
E
I drove the other ones away.

Chorus 1

Emaj7 E7 F♯7aug E
So if you ever feel neglected,
Emaj7 E7 A/C♯ E
And if you think all is lost,
Emaj7 E7 A/C♯ A
Well, I'll be counting up my demons, yeah,
F♯m7/B E
Hoping everything's not lost.

Link 1

𝄆 E* | E7* E6 | E* | E7* E6 𝄇

Verse 2

E G♯dim F♯7aug E
When you thought that it was over,
G♯dim F♯7aug E
You could feel it all around.
G♯dim F♯7aug F♯m7/B
When everybody's out to get you,
E
Don't you let it drag you down.

Chorus 2 As Chorus 1

Link 2 ‖: E* | E7* E6 | E* | E7* E6 :‖

Chorus 3 As Chorus 1

Outro

```
                E*                  E7* E6
Singing out ah, ah ah yeah,   ah ah yeah,
E*              E7*   E6                  E*
Ah ah yeah,   and everything's not lost,
                       E7*  E6         E*
So come on, yeah,   ah ah yeah,
                  E7*    E6                  E*
Come on, yeah,   and everything's not lost.

                E7*  E6          E*
Ah ah yeah,   ah ah yeah,
                E7*    E6                 E*
Ah ah yeah,   and everything's not lost,
                    E7*  E6          E*
Come on yeah,   ah ah yeah,
                       E7*  E6
A-come on yeah.

E                        Bm                 F#m9
   A-come on yeah,   ah ah yeah,
                                              E
Come on yeah, and everything's not lost.
                 Bm                F#m9
Sing out yeah,   ah ah yeah,
                                              E
Come on yeah, and everything's not lost.
                 Bm                F#m9
Come on yeah,   ah ah yeah,
                                             E      Bm    F#m
Sing out yeah, and everything's not lost.
```

Fix You

Words & Music by Guy Berryman, Chris Martin, Jon Buckland & Will Champion

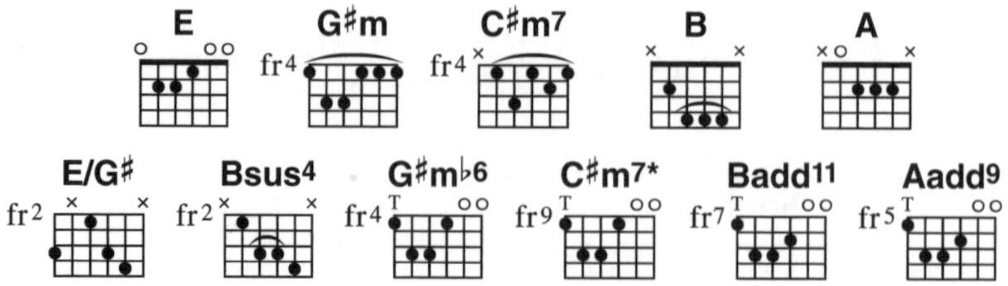

Tune guitar down a semitone

Intro | E G♯m | C♯m7 B | E G♯m | C♯m7 B ||

Verse 1

E G♯m C♯m7 B
When you try your best but you don't succeed,______

E G♯m C♯m7 B
When you get what you want but not what you need,______

E G♯m C♯m7 B
When you feel so tired but you can't sleep,______

E G♯m C♯m7 B
Stuck in re - verse.______

E G♯m C♯m7 B
And the tears come streaming down your face______

E G♯m C♯m7 B
When you lose something you can't replace,______

E G♯m C♯m7 B
When you love someone but it goes to waste...______

E G♯m C♯m7 B
Could it be worse?______

Chorus 1

A E/G♯ Bsus4 B A
Lights will__ guide__ you home

E/G♯ Bsus4 B A
And ig - nite__ your bones,

E/G♯ Bsus4 B
I__ will__ try__ to fix you.

```
Instrumental 1 | E    G#m    | C#m7   B  | E    G#m    | C#m7   B  ||

                 E                    G#m♭6        C#m7*  Badd11
Verse 2          High up above and down below,__________
                          E                 G#m♭6   C#m7*  Badd11
                 When you're too in love to let it go,__________
                        E                  G#m♭6       C#m7*  Badd11
                 But if you never try you'll never know __________
                              E       G#m♭6   C#m7*  Badd11
                 Just what you're worth.__________

                 A         E/G#      Bsus4  B       A
Chorus 2           Lights will___ guide___ you home
                     E/G#    Bsus4   B          A
                 And ig  -  nite_____ your bones,
                     E/G#     Bsus4  B
                 I___ will___ try_____ to fix you.

Instrumental 2 |: E        | Aadd9    | E        | Badd11   |
               | C#m7*     | Aadd9    | E        | Badd11  :|

                 E             Aadd9
Bridge             Tears stream     down your face
                 E                           Badd11
                   When you lose something you cannot replace,
                 C#m7*         Aadd9              E     Badd11
                   Tears stream    down your face and I...______
                 E             Aadd9
                   Tears stream    down your face,
                 E                       Badd11
                   I promise you I will learn from my mistakes.
                 C#m7*         Aadd9                  E  Badd11
                   Tears stream    down your face and I...______

                 A        E/G#     Bsus4  B        A
Outro              Lights will__ guide___ you home
                     E/G#    Bsus4  B         A
                 And ig  -  nite____ your bones,
                        E/G#    Bsus4  B            E
                 And I__ will__ try_____ to fix you.__
```

For You

Words & Music by Guy Berryman, Chris Martin, Jon Buckland & Will Champion

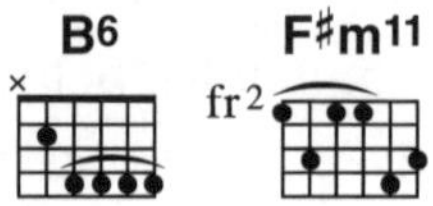

Intro | B6 | B6 |

|: B6 | F♯m11 | B6 | F♯m11 :|

Verse 1

B6 F♯m11
If you're lost and feel alone,
B6 F♯m11
Circumnavigate the globe,
B6 F♯m11
All you ever have to hope for too.
B6 F♯m11
And the way you seem to flow,
B6 F♯m11
Circumnavigate and hope,
B6 F♯m11 B6 F♯m11
And I seem to lose control, with you.

Chorus 1

B6 F♯m11
Ah, __________
B6 F♯m11
Ah, __________
B6 F♯m11
Ah, __________
B6 F♯m11
Ah. __________

Link 1 |: B6 | F♯m11 | B6 | F♯m11 :|

Verse 2

```
B6                       F♯m11
   Every one of us is hurt,
B6                            F♯m11
   And every one of us is scarred,
B6                       F♯m11           B6      F♯m11
   Every one of us is scared but not you.
      B6         F♯m11
And when your eyes close,
B6       F♯m11
   Your head hurts,
B6       F♯m11    B6       F♯m11
   Your eyes like stone.
```

Chorus 2

```
B6        F♯m11
Ah, ____________
B6        F♯m11
Ah, ____________
B6        F♯m11
Ah, ____________
B6        F♯m11
Ah. ____________
```

Link 2

```
| B6          | F♯m11      | B6          | F♯m11     ||
```

Verse 3

```
B6                       F♯m11
   Every one of us is scared,
B6                       F♯m11
   Every one of us is hurt,
B6                   F♯m11    B6      F♯m11
   Every one has hope for you.
```

Outro

```
        B6     F♯m11
||: For you,            :||   Play 6 times
    B6     F♯m11
For you.

| B6          | F♯m11       |

    B6     F♯m11
For you.
    B6     F♯m11
For you.

| B6          | F♯m11       | B6          ||
```

God Put A Smile Upon Your Face

Words & Music by Guy Berryman, Chris Martin, Jon Buckland & Will Champion

D♭ E6 E♭7 Dmaj7 Amaj7 F♯add9

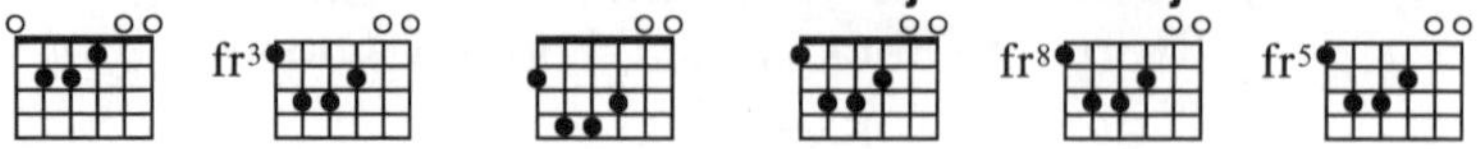

Tune down three semitones

Verse 1

D♭ E6 E♭7 Dmaj7
Where do we go, nobody knows?
D♭ E6 E♭7 Dmaj7
I've gotta say I'm on my way ___ down.
D♭ E6 E♭7 Dmaj7
God give me style and give me grace.
D♭ E6 E♭7 Dmaj7
God put a smile upon my face. _______

Guitar Solo 1

| D♭ | E6 | E♭7 | E♭7 Dmaj7 |
| D♭ | E6 | E♭7 | Dmaj7 ||

Verse 2

D♭ E6 E♭7 Dmaj7
Where do we go to draw the line?
D♭ E6 E♭7 Dmaj7
I've gotta say I've wasted all your time, honey, honey
D♭ E6 E♭7 Dmaj7
Where do I go to fall from grace?
D♭ E6 E♭7 Dmaj7
God put a smile upon your face. Yeah.

Chorus 1

Amaj7 E6 F♯add9 Ama
And ah ____ when you work it out I'm worse than you. ____
E6 F♯add9 Amaj7
Yeah, _____ when you work it out I wanted to. _____
E6 F♯add9 Amaj7
And ah _____ when you work out where to draw the line, _____
E6 F♯add9
Your guess is as good as mine.

```
Guitar Solo 2  | D♭        | E6        | E♭7       | E♭7   Dmaj7 |

               | D♭        | E6        | E♭7       | Dmaj7       ||

               D♭             E6                  E♭7      Dmaj7
Verse 3           Where do we go, nobody knows?
               D♭           E6                   E♭7      Dmaj7
                  Don't ever say you're on your way down.
                  D♭             E6                  E♭7    Dmaj7
               When God gave you style and gave you grace,
               D♭          E6                  E♭7      Dmaj7
                  And put a smile upon your face, ah yeah.

                   Amaj7      E6               F♯add9                Amaj7
Chorus 2       And ah, when you work it out I'm worse than you. ____
                              E6        F♯add9      Amaj7
               Yeah, when you work it out I wanted to. ____
                                E6            F♯add9            Amaj7
               And ah, when you work out where to draw the line, ____
                             E6       F♯add9    D♭    E6    E♭7
               Your guess is as good as mine. ____
                    Dmaj7     D♭     E6    E♭7
               It's as good as mine. ______
                    Dmaj7     D♭     E6    E♭7
               It's as good as mine. ____
                    Dmaj7     D♭     E6
               It's as good as mine. ____
               E♭7
               Na na na na na na na na na na
                    Dmaj7  Amaj7           E6
               It's as good as mine. _________
               F♯add9      Amaj7           E6
               It's as good as mine. _________
               F♯add9      Amaj7   E6      F♯add9
               It's as good as mine. _________

               D♭             E6                  E♭7      Dmaj7
Outro             Where do we go, nobody knows?
               D♭           E6                   E♭7      Dmaj7
                  Don't ever say you're on your way down.
                  D♭             E6                  E♭7    Dmaj7
               When God gave you style and gave you grace,
               D♭          E6                  E♭7      Dmaj7 (fermata)
                  And put a smile upon your face.
```

The Goldrush

Words & Music by Guy Berryman, Chris Martin, Jon Buckland & Will Champion

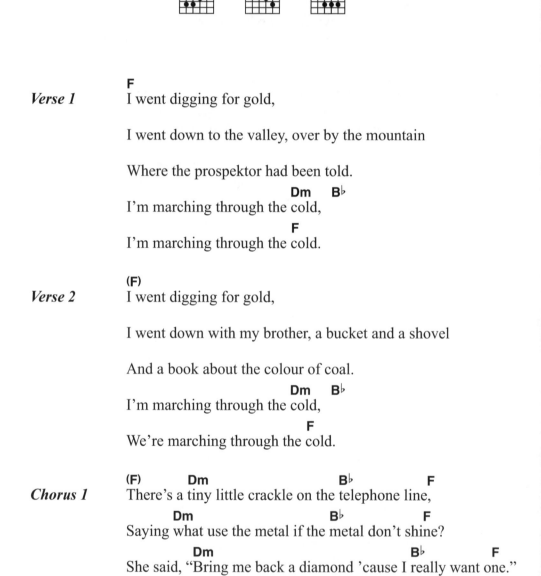

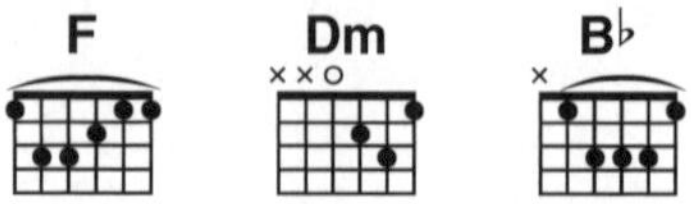


```
               F
*Verse 1*      I went digging for gold,

               I went down to the valley, over by the mountain

               Where the prospektor had been told.
                                           Dm     B♭
               I'm marching through the cold,
                                           F
               I'm marching through the cold.


               (F)
*Verse 2*      I went digging for gold,

               I went down with my brother, a bucket and a shovel

               And a book about the colour of coal.
                                           Dm     B♭
               I'm marching through the cold,
                                             F
               We're marching through the cold.


               (F)       Dm                        B♭          F
*Chorus 1*     There's a tiny little crackle on the telephone line,
                     Dm                          B♭         F
               Saying what use the metal if the metal don't shine?
                         Dm                                 B♭         F
               She said, "Bring me back a diamond 'cause I really want one."
                             Dm                    B♭        F
               Now I've been digging so long that I never see the sun.
```

Verse 3

```
(F)
I went digging for gold,

I went down to the valley, over by the mountain

Where the prospektor had been told.
                               Dm     B♭
I'm marching through the cold,
                                F
We're marching through the cold.
```

Chorus 2

```
(F)     Dm                      B♭        F
There's a tiny little crackle on the telephone line,
    Dm                      B♭        F
Saying what use the metal if the metal don't shine?
          Dm                           B♭        F
She said, "Bring me back a diamond 'cause I really want one."
              Dm                B♭         F
Now I've been digging so long that I never see the sun.
          Dm                B♭         F
I've been digging so long that I never see the sun.
              Dm                B♭         F
Now I've been digging so long that I never see the sun.
```

Gravity

Words & Music by Guy Berryman, Chris Martin, Jon Buckland & Will Champion

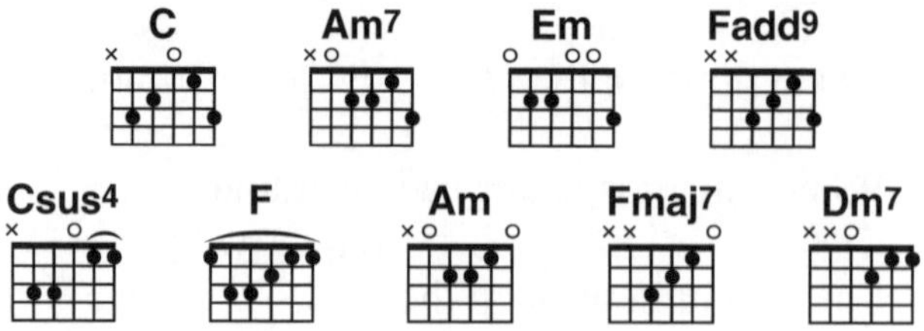

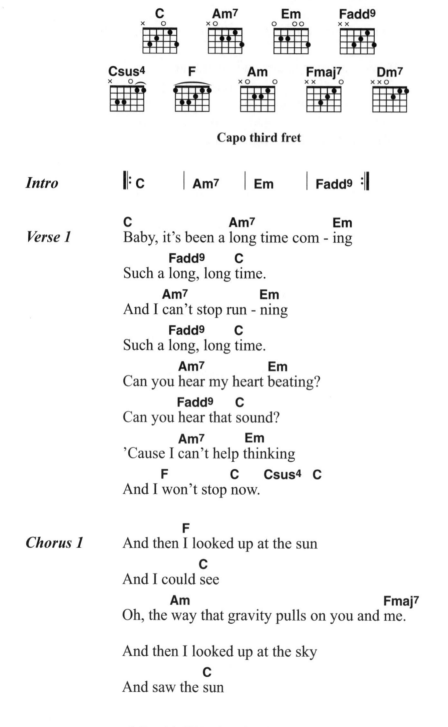

Capo third fret

Intro ‖: C | Am7 | Em | Fadd9 :‖

Verse 1

C Am7 Em
Baby, it's been a long time com - ing

Fadd9 C
Such a long, long time.

Am7 Em
And I can't stop run - ning

Fadd9 C
Such a long, long time.

Am7 Em
Can you hear my heart beating?

Fadd9 C
Can you hear that sound?

Am7 Em
'Cause I can't help thinking

F C Csus4 C
And I won't stop now.

Chorus 1

F
And then I looked up at the sun

C
And I could see

Am Fmaj7
Oh, the way that gravity pulls on you and me.

And then I looked up at the sky

C
And saw the sun

cont.

                Am   Fmaj7
And the way that gravity pushes on every - one.
                     Dm7
On every - one.

Verse 2

C   Am7   Em
Baby, when your wheels stop turning
                    Fadd9 C
And you feel let down.
              Am7   Em
And it seems like troubles
                      Fadd9   C
Have come all—— a - round.
          Am7   Em
I can hear your heart beating
          Fadd9   C
I can hear that sound.
          Am7   Em
But I can't help thinking
              Fadd9   C   Csus4   C
And I won't look now.

Chorus 2

                    F
And then I looked up at the sun
                      C
And I could see
              Am   Fmaj7
Oh, the way that gravity pulls on you and me.

And then I looked up at the sky
                      C
And saw the sun
                Am   Fmaj7
And the way that gravity pushes on every - one.
                     Dm7
On every - one.

On everyone.

Outro

𝄆 C | Am7 | Em | Fadd9 𝄇 *Play 4 times*

| C ‖

Green Eyes

Words & Music by Guy Berryman, Chris Martin, Jon Buckland & Will Champion

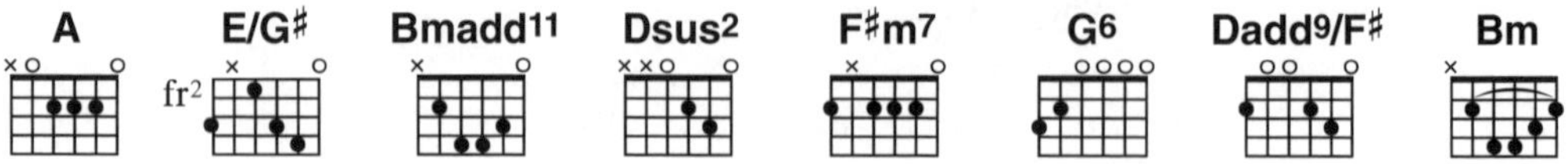

Verse 1

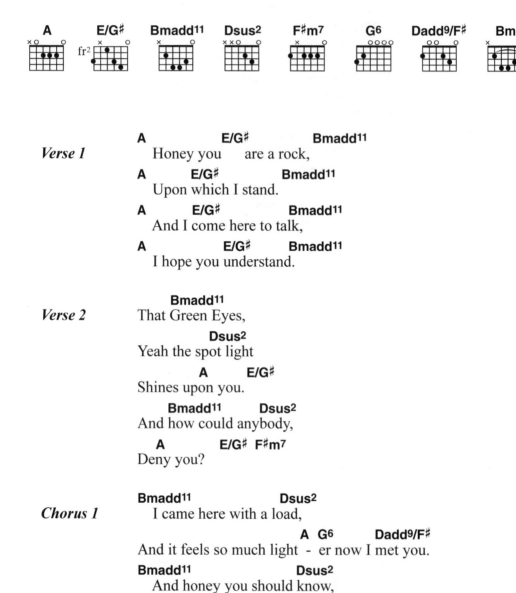

A E/G♯ Bmadd11
Honey you are a rock,
A E/G♯ Bmadd11
Upon which I stand.
A E/G♯ Bmadd11
And I come here to talk,
A E/G♯ Bmadd11
I hope you understand.

Verse 2

Bmadd11
That Green Eyes,
Dsus2
Yeah the spot light
A E/G♯
Shines upon you.
Bmadd11 Dsus2
And how could anybody,
A E/G♯ F♯m7
Deny you?

Chorus 1

Bmadd11 Dsus2
I came here with a load,
A G6 Dadd9/F♯
And it feels so much light - er now I met you.
Bmadd11 Dsus2
And honey you should know,
A G6 Dsus2
That I could never go on without you.
Bmadd11 | Bmadd11 | Bmadd11 | Bmadd11 ||
Green Eyes.

Verse 3

```
A               E/G♯          Bmadd11
   Honey you     are the sea,
A       E/G♯          Bmadd11
   Upon which I float.
A          E/G♯             Bmadd11
   And I came here to talk,
A           E/G♯            Bmadd11
   I think you should know.
```

Verse 4

```
      Bmadd11
That Green Eyes,
             Dsus2                A        E/G♯
You're the one that I wanted to find.
           Bmadd11
And any-one who
             Dsus2
Tried to deny you
                   A            E/G♯  F♯m7
Must be out of their minds.
```

Chorus 2

```
Bmadd11                                Dsus2
   Because I came here with a load,
                             A  G6          Dadd9/F♯
And it feels so much light  -  er since I met you.
Bmadd11                Dsus2
   And honey you should know,
                        A     G6      Dsus2
That I could never go on     without you.
Bm
Green Eyes,

Green Eyes,
         A
Oh oh oh.
         Bm
Oh oh oh.

Oh oh oh.
```

Outro

```
A               E/G♯          Bmadd11
   Honey you     are a rock
A          E/G♯        Bmadd11
   Upon which I stand.
```

The Hardest Part

Words & Music by Guy Berryman, Chris Martin, Jon Buckland & Will Champion

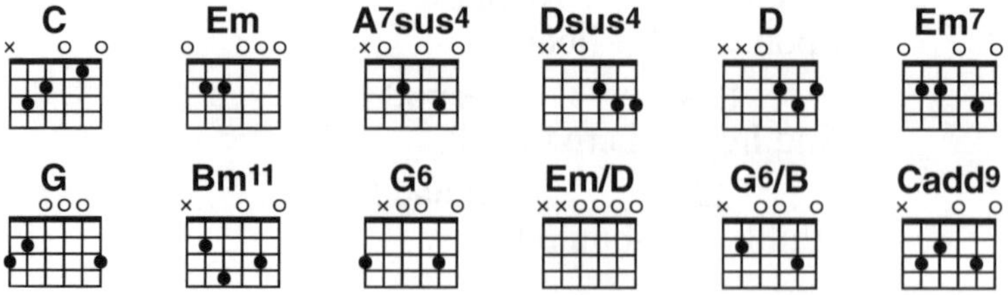

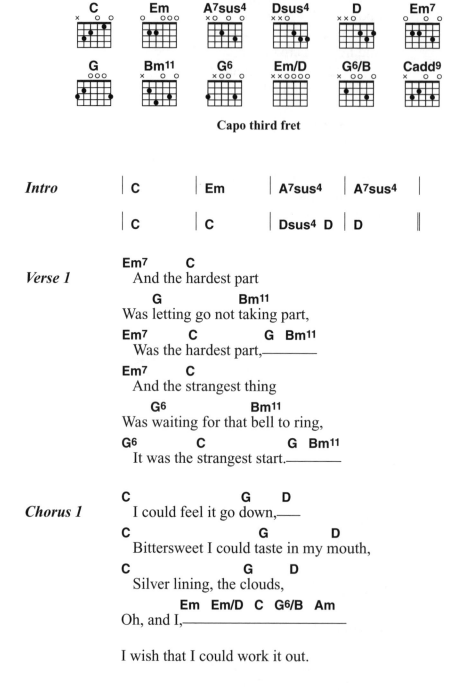

Capo third fret

Intro | C | Em | A7sus4 | A7sus4 |
| C | C | Dsus4 D | D ||

Verse 1

Em7 C
And the hardest part
G Bm11
Was letting go not taking part,
Em7 C G Bm11
Was the hardest part,______
Em7 C
And the strangest thing
G6 Bm11
Was waiting for that bell to ring,
G6 C G Bm11
It was the strangest start.______

Chorus 1

C G D
I could feel it go down,__
C G D
Bittersweet I could taste in my mouth,
C G D
Silver lining, the clouds,
Em Em/D C G6/B Am
Oh, and I,______________

I wish that I could work it out.

Verse 2

```
Em7       C
   And the hardest part
       G                 Bm11
Was letting go not taking part,
Em7          C          G     Bm11
   You really broke my heart.___
Em7       C
   And I tried to sing
        G6                    Bm11
But I couldn't think of anything,
G6             C            G    Bm11
   It was the hardest part.______
```

Chorus 2

```
C                       G      D
   I could feel it go down,__
C                           G            D
   You left the sweetest taste in my mouth,
C                     G        D
   Silver lining, the clouds,
            Em   Em/D  C  G6/B  Am
Oh, and I,__________________________
            Em   Em/D  C  G6/B  D
Oh, and I,__________________________

I wonder what it's all about.
```

Instrumental 2

```
||: C          | Em         | A7sus4     | A7sus4     :||  Play 3 times
|   C          | C          | D          | D          ||
```

Bridge

```
                C      Em     A7sus4
Everything I know is___ wrong,
               C          Em            A7sus4
Everything I do it just comes un - done,
                C     Em   A7sus4
Everything is torn apart,_____
                       C
Oh, and that's the hardest part.
               Dsus4       D
That's the hardest part,___
                    C
Yeah, that's the hardest part,
               Dsus4      D
That's the hardest part.
```

Outro

```
||: C          | Em         | A7sus4     | A7sus4     :||  Play 4 times to fade
```

Help Is Round The Corner

Words & Music by Guy Berryman, Chris Martin, Jon Buckland & Will Champion

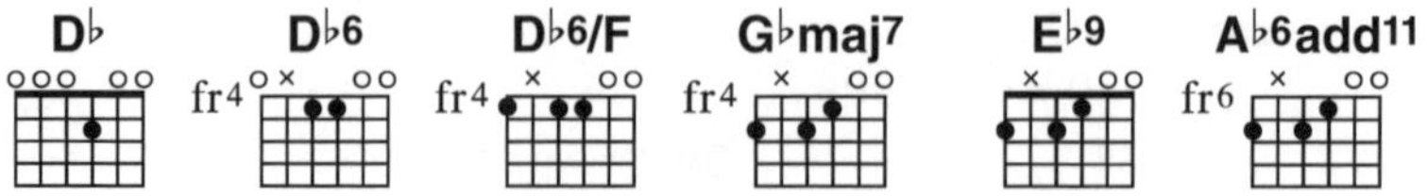

Tune guitar (from bottom string): D♭, A♭, D♭, G♭, D♭, F

Intro | D♭ | D♭6 | D♭ | D♭6 ||

Verse 1

D♭   D♭6
Stuck here in the middle of nowhere
             D♭   D♭6
With a headache, and a heavy heart.
           D♭   D♭6
Well, nothing was going quite right here,
                 D♭   D♭6   D♭6/F
And I'm tired, I can't play my part.

Chorus 1

G♭maj7
    Oh, come on, come on,
                   E♭9
Oh what a state I'm in,
G♭maj7
    Oh, come on, come on,
                        E♭9
Why won't it just sink in
          D♭   A♭6add11   D♭   A♭6add11
That help is just around the corner for us?

Verse 2

       D♭   D♭6
Oh, my head just won't stop aching,
               D♭   D♭6
And I'm sat here licking my wounds
               D♭   D♭6
And I'm shattered, but it really doesn't matter
                   D♭   D♭6   D♭6/F
'Cause my rescue is gonna be here soon.

Chorus 2

```
Gbmaj7
    Oh, come on, come on,
                  Eb9
Oh what a state I'm in,
Gbmaj7
    Oh, come on, come on,
                      Eb9
Why won't it just sink in
        Db                         Ab6add11      Db      Ab6add11
That help is just around the corner for us? ____
        Db                         Ab6add11      Db      Eb9
That help is just around the corner for us. ____
             Gbmaj7                     Ab6add11      Db
Oh, that help is just around the corner for us. ____
```

High Speed

Words & Music by Guy Berryman, Chris Martin, Jon Buckland & Will Champion

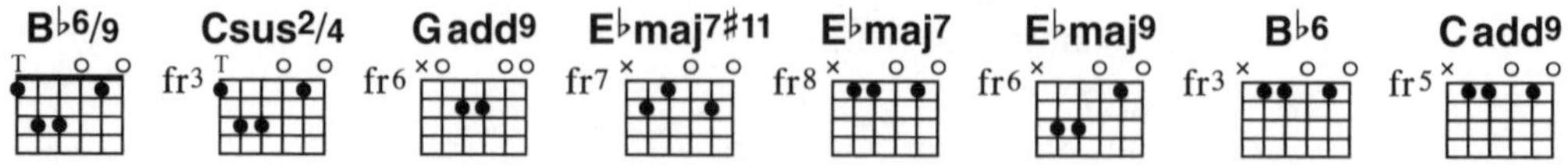

Tune guitar (from bottom string): D, G, D, G, B, D

Intro

|: B♭6/9 | Csus2/4 | B♭6/9 | Csus2/4 :|

| Gadd9 | Gadd9 | Gadd9 | Gadd9 ||

Verse 1

```
E♭maj7♯11                Gadd9     E♭maj7♯11
   Can anybody fly this thing?

Before my head explodes,
   E♭maj7          E♭maj9     Gadd9
Before my head starts to  ring.
E♭maj7                     E♭maj9            Gadd9   B♭6
   We've been living life   inside a bubble,
                                 Cadd9    Gadd9
We've been living life inside a bubble.
```

Chorus 1

```
B♭6/9                  Csus2/4
   And confidence in you
                   B♭6/9
Is confidence in me,
                   Csus2/4   Gadd9
Is confidence in high           speed.
```

Verse 2

```
E♭maj7♯11                   Gadd9     E♭maj7♯11
   Can anybody stop this thing?

Before my head explodes,
   E♭maj7          E♭maj9     Gadd9
Before my head starts to  ring.
E♭maj7                     E♭maj9            Gadd9   B♭6
   We've been living life   inside a bubble,
                                 Cadd9    Gadd9
We've been living life inside a bubble.
```

Chorus 2

```
Bb6/9                  Csus2/4
   And confidence in you
                Bb6/9
Is confidence in me,
                Csus2/4  Gadd9
Is confidence in high    speed,

In high speed, high speed.
```

Link

```
| Gadd9  | Gadd9  | Gadd9  | Gadd9  ||
```

Outro

```
Bb6/9           Csus2/4      Bb6/9
   And high speed you want,
         Csus2/4       Bb6/9
High speed you want,
         Csus2/4       Bb6/9   Csus2/4
High speed you want,
                       Gadd9
High speed you want.

||: Gadd9  | Gadd9  :||  Repeat to fade
```

How You See The World No. 2

Words & Music by Guy Berryman, Chris Martin, Jon Buckland & Will Champion

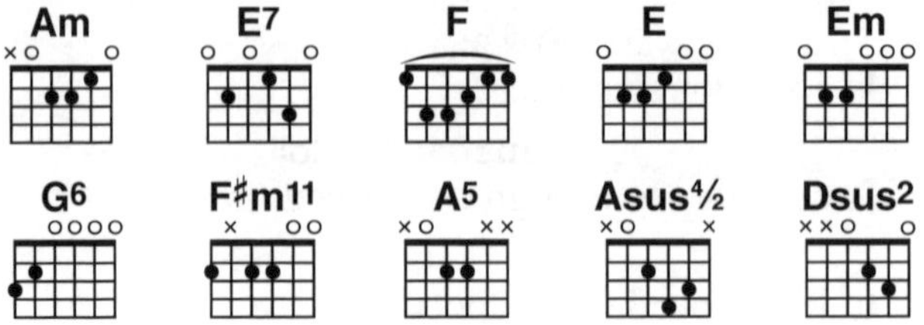

Tune guitar down a semitone

Verse 1

Am
They put the world in a tin can
E7
Black market contraband.
Am
And it hurt just a little bit
E7
When they sliced and packaged it.
Am
In a long black trench coat
E7
Two hands around the throat
F Am E
Oh, you wanna get it right some - times.

Verse 2

Am
There's so much to be scared of
E7
And not much to make sense of.
Am
How did the clowns ever get control?
E7
But if you hear can you let me know.
Am
How can they invade it
E7
When it's so complicated?
F Am E
Oh, you wanna get it right some - times.
F Am E
You just wanna get it right some - times.

Chorus 1

```
F                            Am
   It's how you see the world
               Em
How many times can you say
                  F
You can't be - lieve what you heard.
                             Am
   It's how you see the world
              G6
Don't you worry yourself
               F#m11
You're not gonna get hurt.
F        E
Ooh...
```

Link 1

```
||: Am   | Am   | E7   | E7   :||
```

Verse 3

```
                Am
And there's something missing
                         E7
Seems like there's nobody listening.
             Am
If you're running in a circle
                  E7
How can you be too careful?
             Am
We don't wanna be mantrapped
             E7
We don't wanna be shrink wrapped.
    F                       Am          E
Oh,   just wanna get it right some - times.
F                            Am          E
   You just wanna get it right some - times.
```

Chorus 2

```
F                        Am
   That's how you see the world
            Em
How many times have you heard
          F
That you can't believe a word?
                         Am
   That's how you see the world
           G6
Don't you worry yourself
             F#m11
'Cause no - body can hurt.
F      E7
You..

| F   E7  | F   E7  ||
```

Link 2

```
||: A5  Asus4/2 | A5        | A5  Asus4/2 | A5        :||
```

Outro

```
||: F   Dsus2   | Dsus2     | A5  Asus4/2 | A5        :||

F          Dsus2          A5       Asus4/2  A5
   That's how you see the world.
F          Dsus2          A5       Asus4/2
   That's how you see the world.
```

I Bloom Blaum

Words & Music by Guy Berryman, Chris Martin, Jon Buckland & Will Champion

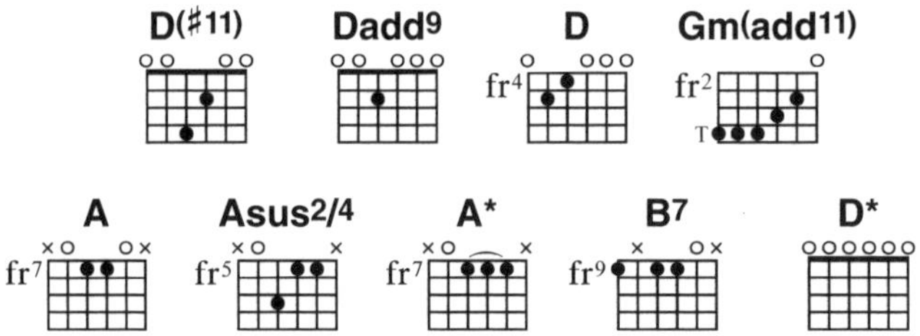

Tune guitar (from bottom string): D, A, D, F♯, A, D

Intro

D(♯11)	Dadd9 D(♯11)	D(♯11)	Dadd9 D(♯11)
D(♯11)	Dadd9 D(♯11)	D(♯11)	Dadd9 D(♯11)
D	D	D(♯11)	Dadd9 D(♯11)
D(♯11)	Dadd9 D(♯11)	Gm(add11)	Gm(add11)

Verse

```
Gm(add11)                 D(♯11)
Darling, those tired eyes
Gm(add11)                  D(♯11)
    Go with me all the time.
Gm(add11)                      D(♯11)
    And in the dead of night
Gm(add11)                      D(♯11)
    Tell me you will be mine.
A                Asus2/4  A*        Asus2/4
Where do you go to,        pretty baby?
A                Asus2/4             A*          Asus2/4
Where do you go to, when the night wins away.
A               Asus2/4  A*          Asus2/4
  Ask me so sweetly,     what do I do?
A              Asus2/4
  Who do I sing for?
      A*       Asus2/4       B7               Gm(add11)          D(♯11)
Well honey I sing about you. ______________________________________
B7            Gm(add11)      D(♯11)        D
You. ________________________________________
```

In My Place

Words & Music by Guy Berryman, Chris Martin, Jon Buckland & Will Champion

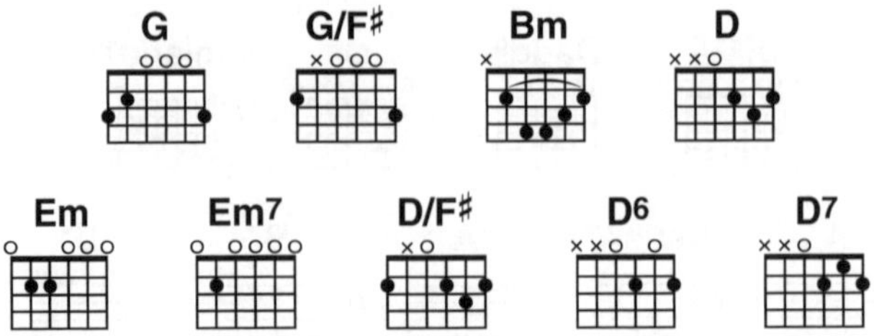

Capo second fret

Intro ‖: G G/F♯ | Bm D | G Em | Bm D :‖

Verse 1

G G/F♯ Bm D G
In my place, in my place were lines that I couldn't change

Em7 Bm D
I was lost, oh yeah.

G G/F♯ Bm D G
And I was lost, I was lost, crossed lines I shouldn't have crossed

Em Bm D
I was lost, oh yeah.

Chorus 1

C G D/F♯ C
Yeah, how long must you wait for it?

G D/F♯ C
Yeah, how long must you pay for it?

G D/F♯ C
Yeah, how long must you wait for it?

D
Ah, for it?

Link | G G/F♯ | Bm D | G Em | Bm D ‖

Verse 2

G G/F♯ Bm D G
I was scared, I was scared, tired and under-prepared,

Em7 Bm D
But I'll wait for it.

G G/F♯ Bm D G
And if you go, if you go and leave me down here on my own,

Em Bm D
Then I'll wait for you, yeah.

Chorus 2

C G D/F♯ C
Yeah, how long must you wait for it?

G D/F♯ C
Yeah, how long must you pay for it?

G D/F♯ C
Yeah, how long must you wait for it?

D
Ah, for it?

Instrumental ‖: G G/F♯ | Bm D | G Em | Bm D :‖

Middle

G G/F♯ Bm
Singing: "Please, please, please,

D G Em Bm
Come back and sing to me, to me, ah me.

D G G/F♯ Bm
Come on and sing it out, now, now

D G Em Bm
Come on and sing it out, to me, ah me

D
Come back and sing it."

Outro

G G/F♯ Bm D G
In my place, in my place were lines that I couldn't change

Em7 D6
I was lost, oh yeah.

D7 G
Oh yeah.

I Ran Away

Words & Music by Guy Berryman, Chris Martin, Jon Buckland & Will Champion

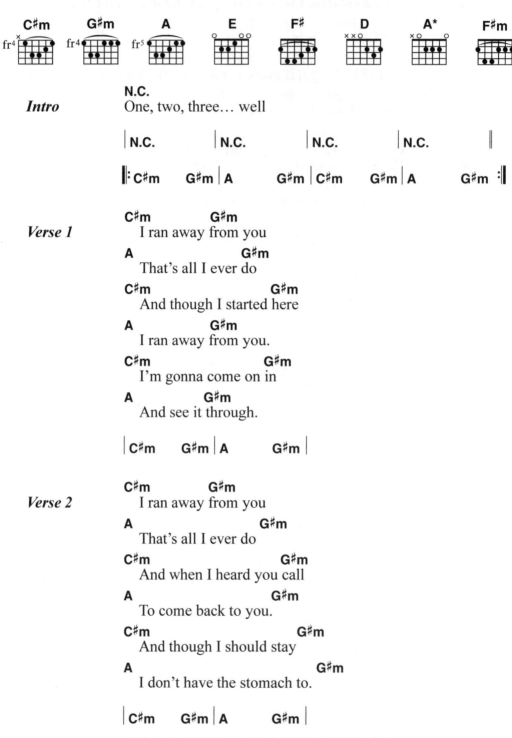

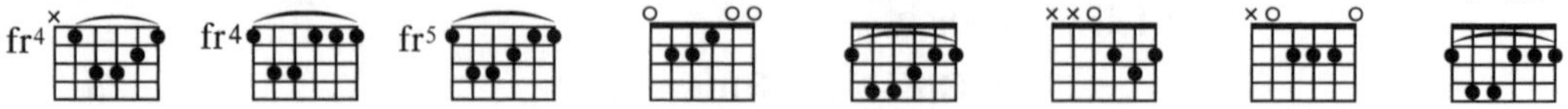

Intro

N.C.
One, two, three… well

| N.C. | N.C. | N.C. | N.C. ||

|: C♯m G♯m | A G♯m | C♯m G♯m | A G♯m :|

Verse 1

C♯m G♯m
I ran away from you
A G♯m
That's all I ever do
C♯m G♯m
And though I started here
A G♯m
I ran away from you.
C♯m G♯m
I'm gonna come on in
A G♯m
And see it through.

| C♯m G♯m | A G♯m |

Verse 2

C♯m G♯m
I ran away from you
A G♯m
That's all I ever do
C♯m G♯m
And when I heard you call
A G♯m
To come back to you.
C♯m G♯m
And though I should stay
A G♯m
I don't have the stomach to.

| C♯m G♯m | A G♯m |

```
             E        F♯
*Chorus 1*      Everyone I know,
                          D                        A*
             Says I'm a fool to mess with you,
             E        F♯
                Everyone I know
                         D                 A*
             Says it's a stupid thing to do.
             E                F♯
                I have your love on call
                            D            A*
             And yet my day was so full
                                 D                  A*
             There might be nothing left to do
                 D                  A*
             So I ran away from you.
```

```
*Link*       ||: C♯m    G♯m | A       G♯m | C♯m    G♯m | A       G♯m  :||
```

```
             C♯m                    G♯m
*Verse 3*       I'm gonna come on in
             A              G♯m
                My eyes are closed.
             C♯m              G♯m
                I can feel it there
             A                G♯m
                The sun's so close.
             C♯m                G♯m
                I'm gonna come on out
             A              G♯m
                And burn the sky.

             | C♯m    G♯m | A       G♯m |
```

```
             C♯m        G♯m
*Verse 4*       A star arose,
             A              G♯m
                In my own cage
             C♯m              G♯m
                I'm stuck in line
             A             G♯m
                And in a cage
             C♯m                 G♯m
                Just a single star
             A              G♯m
                I see it fall.
```

cont. | C♯m G♯m | A G♯m |

Chorus 2

```
E          F♯
   Everyone I know,
              D                        A*
Says I'm a fool to mess with you,
E          F♯
   Everyone I know
             D                   A*
Says it's a stupid thing to do.
E                  F♯
   I have your love on call
               D             A*
And yet my day was so full
                     D                A*
There might be nothing left to do
      D                 A*
So I ran away from you.
```

Outro

```
                          x7
|: C♯m     | F♯m     :| C♯m     | A       |
                                          x3
|: E       | F♯      | D        | A      :|

| D        | A       | D        | A       ||
```

Life In Technicolor

Words & Music by Guy Berryman, Chris Martin, Jon Buckland, Will Champion & Jon Hopkins

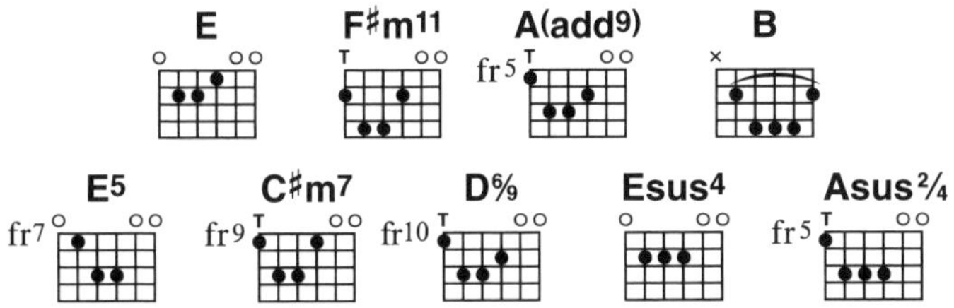

fade in

F♯m11 A(add9)	A(add9) B	B C♯m7	F♯m11 A(add9)
A(add9) B	E5 C♯m7	F♯m11 A(add9)	A(add9)
A(add9)	A(add9)	

Part 1

||: A(add9) | A(add9) | A(add9) | A(add9) :||
||: F♯m11 | D6/9 | A(add9) | A(add9) :||
Play 3 times

Esus4	E	A(add9)	A(add9)	
|: A(add9)	Asus2/4	A(add9)	Asus2/4 :|
F♯m11	D6/9	A(add9)	A(add9)
Esus4	E	A(add9)	A(add9)	

Part 2

| F♯m11 | D6/9 | C♯m7 | C♯m7 |
Oh,

| F♯m11 | D6/9 | C♯m7 | C♯m7 |
Oh,——— oh, ——— Oh.———

F♯m11	D6/9	A(add9)	F♯m11
Esus4	E	A(add9)	A(add9)
A(add9)	

Life In Technicolor II

Words & Music by Guy Berryman, Chris Martin, Jon Buckland, Will Champion & Jon Hopkins

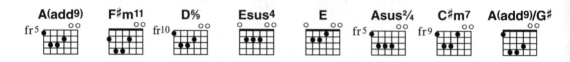

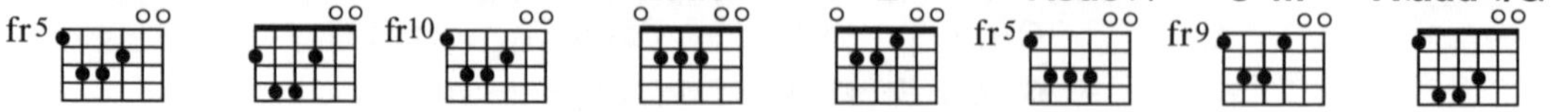

Intro

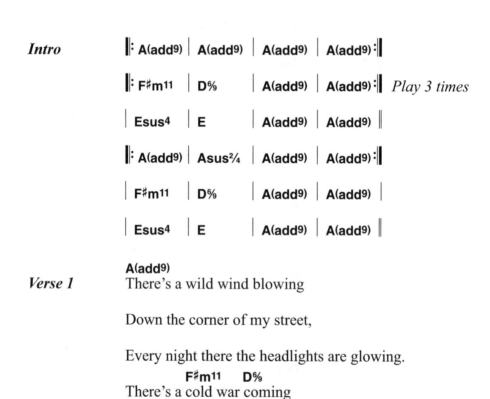

|: A(add9) | A(add9) | A(add9) | A(add9) :|

|: F#m11 | D6/9 | A(add9) | A(add9) :| *Play 3 times*

| Esus4 | E | A(add9) | A(add9) ||

|: A(add9) | Asus2/4 | A(add9) | A(add9) :|

| F#m11 | D6/9 | A(add9) | A(add9) |

| Esus4 | E | A(add9) | A(add9) ||

Verse 1

```
A(add9)
There's a wild wind blowing

Down the corner of my street,

Every night there the headlights are glowing.
                F#m11      D6/9
There's a cold war coming
          A(add9)
On the radio I heard,
Esus4         E        A(add9)
Baby, it's a violent world.
```

Chorus 1

F♯m11 D6/9 C♯m7
Oh, love don't let me go,

F♯m11 D6/9 C♯m7
Won't you take me where the streetlights glow?

F♯m11 D6/9
I can hear it coming,

A(add9) A(add9)/G♯ F♯m11
I can hear the sirens sound,

Esus4 E A(add9)
Now my feet won't touch the ground.

Link 1

‖: F♯m11 | D6/9 | A(add9) | A(add9) :‖

Verse 2

F♯m11 D6/9
Time came a - creeping,

A(add9)
Oh, and time's a loaded gun,

F♯m11 D6/9 A(add9)
Every road is a ray of light.

F♯m11 D6/9
It goes on,______

A(add9)
Time only can lead you on,

Esus4 E A(add9)
Still it's such a beautiful night.

Chorus 2

F♯m11 D6/9 C♯m7
Oh, love don't let me go,

F♯m11 D6/9 C♯m7
Won't you take me where the streetlights glow?

F♯m11 D6/9
I can hear it coming

A(add9) A(add9)/G♯ F♯m11
Like a sere - nade of sound,

Esus4 E A(add9)
Now my feet won't touch the ground.

Chorus 3

| F♯m11 | D6/9 | C♯m7 | C♯m7 |

F♯m11 D6/9 C♯m7
Oh, oh, oh.

F♯m11 D6/9
Gravity re - lease me

A(add9) A(add9)G♯ F♯m11
And don't ever hold me down,

Esus4 E A(add9)
Now my feet won't touch the ground.

Life Is For Living

Words & Music by Guy Berryman, Chris Martin, Jon Buckland & Will Champion

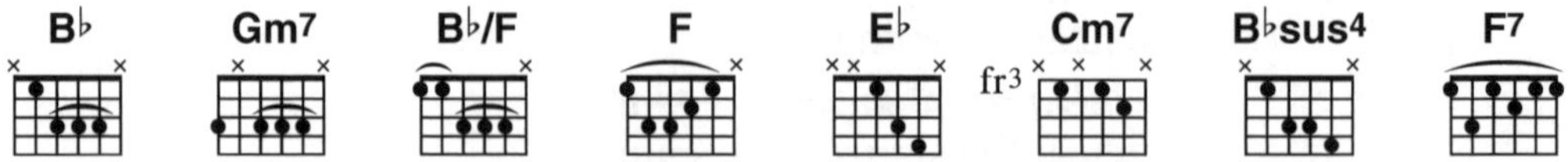

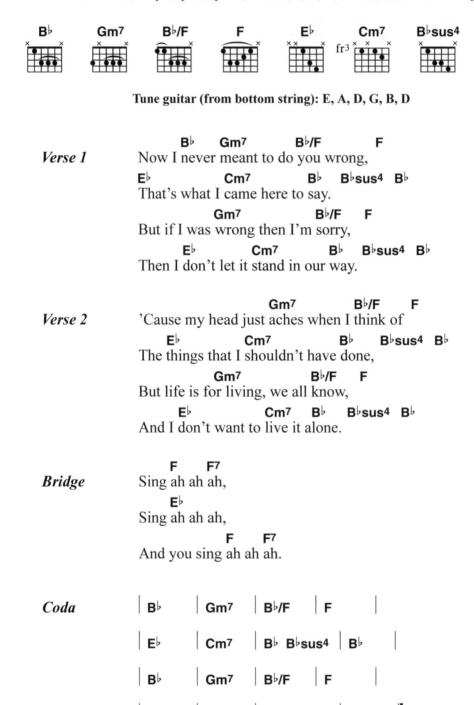

Tune guitar (from bottom string): E, A, D, G, B, D

Verse 1

B♭ Gm7 B♭/F F
Now I never meant to do you wrong,
E♭ Cm7 B♭ B♭sus4 B♭
That's what I came here to say.
Gm7 B♭/F F
But if I was wrong then I'm sorry,
E♭ Cm7 B♭ B♭sus4 B♭
Then I don't let it stand in our way.

Verse 2

Gm7 B♭/F F
'Cause my head just aches when I think of
E♭ Cm7 B♭ B♭sus4 B♭
The things that I shouldn't have done,
Gm7 B♭/F F
But life is for living, we all know,
E♭ Cm7 B♭ B♭sus4 B♭
And I don't want to live it alone.

Bridge

F F7
Sing ah ah ah,
E♭
Sing ah ah ah,
F F7
And you sing ah ah ah.

Coda

B♭	Gm7	B♭/F	F
E♭	Cm7	B♭ B♭sus4	B♭
B♭	Gm7	B♭/F	F
E♭	Cm7	B♭ B♭sus4	B♭	

Lost+

Words & Music by Guy Berryman, Chris Martin, Jon Buckland, Will Champion & Shawn Carter

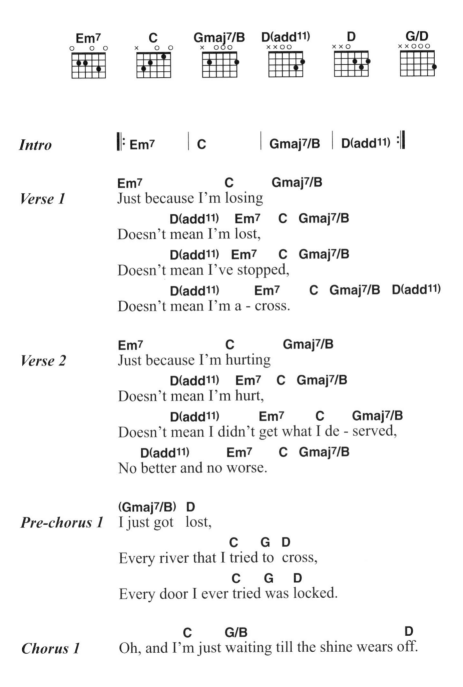

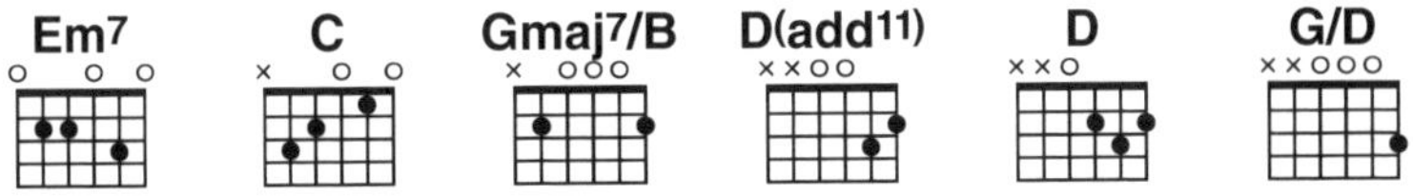

Intro ‖: Em7 | C | Gmaj7/B | D(add11) :‖

Verse 1

Em7 C Gmaj7/B
Just because I'm losing
D(add11) Em7 C Gmaj7/B
Doesn't mean I'm lost,
D(add11) Em7 C Gmaj7/B
Doesn't mean I've stopped,
D(add11) Em7 C Gmaj7/B D(add11)
Doesn't mean I'm a - cross.

Verse 2

Em7 C Gmaj7/B
Just because I'm hurting
D(add11) Em7 C Gmaj7/B
Doesn't mean I'm hurt,
D(add11) Em7 C Gmaj7/B
Doesn't mean I didn't get what I de - served,
D(add11) Em7 C Gmaj7/B
No better and no worse.

Pre-chorus 1

(Gmaj7/B) D
I just got lost,
C G D
Every river that I tried to cross,
C G D
Every door I ever tried was locked.

Chorus 1

C G/B D
Oh, and I'm just waiting till the shine wears off.

Verse 3

Em7 C Gmaj7/B
You might be a big fish

D(add11) Em7 C Gmaj7/B
In a little pond,

D(add11) Em7
Doesn't mean you've won,

C Gmaj7/B D(add11) Em7 C Gmaj7/B
'Cause a - long may come a bigger one.

Pre-chorus 2

Gmaj7/B D
And you'll be lost,

C G D
Every river that you tried to cross,

C G D
Every gun you ever held went off.

Chorus 2

C G/B D
Oh, and I'm just waiting till the firing's stopped.

C G/B D
Oh, and I'm just waiting till the shine wears off.

Jay-Z Rap

(D)
Aha, I gotcha, uh.

Em7
With the same sword they knight you,

C Gmaj7/B
They gon' good-night you with.

D(add11)
Shit, that's only half if they like you.

Em7 C
That ain't even the half what they might do.

Gmaj7/B D(add11)
Don't believe me, ask Michael,

Em7 C Gmaj7/B
See Martin, see Malcolm, see Biggie, see Pac,

D(add11)
See suc - cess and its outcome.

Em7 C Gmaj7/B
See Jesus, see Judas, see Caesar, see Brutus,

D(add11) Em7 C
See suc - cess is like suicide, suicide, it's a suicide.

Gmaj7/B D(add11)
If you suc - ceed, prepare to be crucified.

cont.

```
    Em7                  C
Uh.    Media meddles, niggaz sue you, you settle.
Gmaj7/B                           D(add11)
Every step you take, they re - mind you you're ghetto.
Em7                     C
   So it's tough being Bobby Brown,
        Gmaj7/B                      D(add11)
To be Bobby then, you have to be Bobby now.
          Em7
And the question is,
            C                    Gmaj7/B
Is to have had and lost better than not having at all?

Because,
```

Chorus 2

```
(Gmaj7/B)   C      G/B                          D
Oh and     I'm just waiting till the shine wears off.
            C      G/B                         D
Oh and I'm just waiting till the shine wears off.
C   G/B  D
Oh, oh, oh.
    C   G/B  D
Oh, oh, oh, oh.
```

Outro

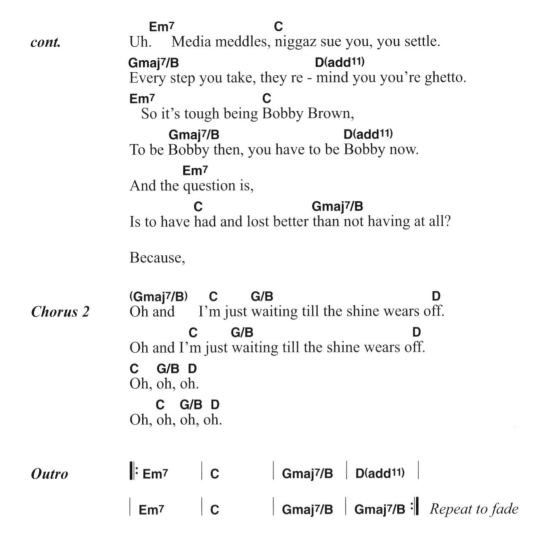

```
|: Em7     | C        | Gmaj7/B  | D(add11)  |
|  Em7     | C        | Gmaj7/B  | Gmaj7/B  :|
```
Repeat to fade

Lost!

Words & Music by Guy Berryman, Chris Martin, Jon Buckland & Will Champion

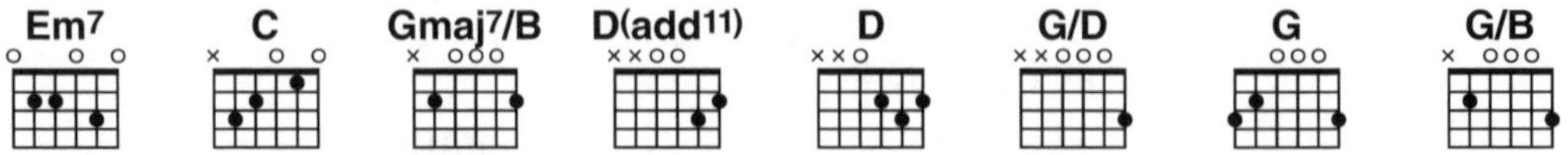


```
Intro        |: Em7    | C      | Gmaj7/B | D(add11) :|

             Em7               C          Gmaj7/B
Verse 1      Just because I'm losing,
                         D(add11)  Em7    C  Gmaj7/B
             Doesn't mean I'm lost,
                         D(add11)  Em7    C  Gmaj7/B
             Doesn't mean I'll stop,
                         D(add11)      Em7   C  Gmaj7/B  D(add11)
             Doesn't mean I'm a - cross.

             Em7               C           Gmaj7/B
Verse 2      Just because I'm hurting,
                         D(add11)  Em7    C  Gmaj7/B
             Doesn't mean I'm hurt,
                         D(add11)        Em7      C      Gmaj7/B
             Doesn't mean I didn't get what I de - served,
                     D(add11)      Em7   C  Gmaj7/B
             No better and no worse.

             Gmaj7/B  D
Pre-chorus 1 I just got lost.
                                   C    G  D
             Every river that I tried to  cross,
                                    C    G    D
             Every door I ever tried was locked.

                         C        G/B                            D
Chorus 1     Oh, and I'm just waiting till the shine wears off.
```

Verse 3

```
Em7                 C        Gmaj7/B
You might be a big fish,
     D(add11)  Em7     C  Gmaj7/B
In a little       pond,
          D(add11)        Em7
Doesn't mean you've won,
              C     Gmaj7/B      D(add11)  Em7   C  Gmaj7/B
'Cause a - long may come a bigger      one.
```

Pre-chorus 2

```
Gmaj7/B       D
And you'll be lost.
                         C    G  D
Every river that you tried to  cross,
                         C    G    D
Every gun you ever held went off.
```

Chorus 2

```
          C        G/B                         D
Oh, and I'm just waiting till the firing's stopped.
          C        G/B                            D
Oh, and I'm just waiting till the shine wears off.
```

Instr.

```
|: Em7   | C     | Gmaj7/B | D(add11) :|
|  Em7   | C     | Gmaj7/B | D(add11)  |
|  Em7   | C     | Gmaj7/B | Gmaj7/B  ||
```

Chorus 3

```
(Gmaj7/B)  C        G/B                           D
Oh, and     I'm just waiting till the shine wears off.
          C        G/B                            D
Oh, and I'm just waiting till the shine wears off.
C    G/B   D
Oh, oh,  oh.
     C   G/B    D
Oh, oh, oh,    oh.
```

Outro

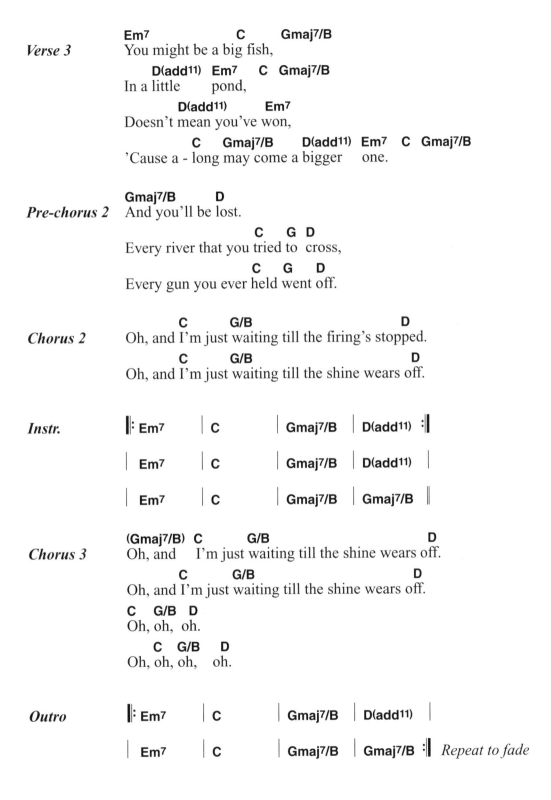

```
|: Em7   | C     | Gmaj7/B | D(add11)  |
|  Em7   | C     | Gmaj7/B | Gmaj7/B  :|  Repeat to fade
```

Lovers In Japan

Words & Music by Guy Berryman, Chris Martin, Jon Buckland & Will Champion

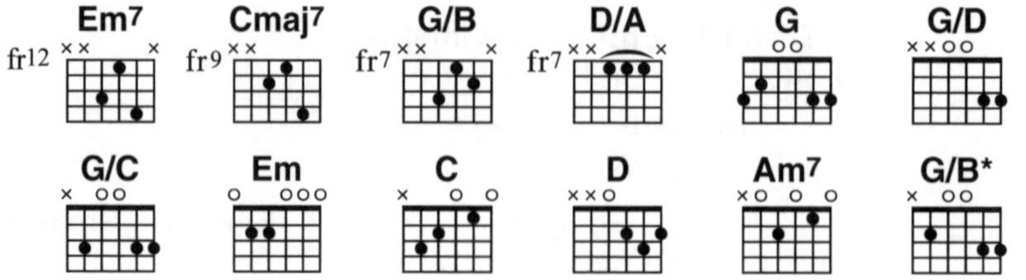

Intro

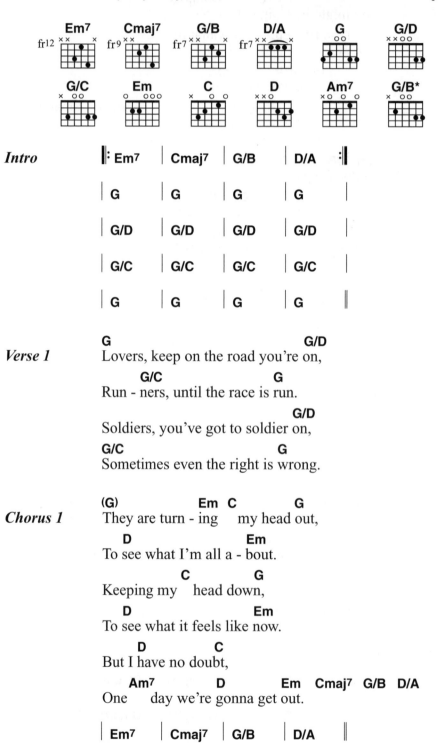

```
|: Em7   | Cmaj7 | G/B   | D/A   :|
|  G     | G     | G     | G     |
|  G/D   | G/D   | G/D   | G/D   |
|  G/C   | G/C   | G/C   | G/C   |
|  G     | G     | G     | G     ||
```

Verse 1

```
G                                  G/D
Lovers, keep on the road you're on,
          G/C                 G
Run - ners, until the race is run.
                                G/D
Soldiers, you've got to soldier on,
G/C                           G
Sometimes even the right is wrong.
```

Chorus 1

```
(G)                 Em  C          G
They are turn - ing     my head out,
    D                    Em
To see what I'm all a - bout.
              C          G
Keeping my    head down,
    D                     Em
To see what it feels like now.
       D           C
But I have no doubt,
    Am7          D          Em   Cmaj7  G/B  D/A
One      day we're gonna get out.

| Em7   | Cmaj7 | G/B   | D/A   ||
```

Verse 2

```
    G                                   G/D
To - night maybe we're gonna run,
           G/C               G
Dream - ing of the Osaka sun.
          G/D
Oh, oh,——
           G/C                                G
Dream - ing of when the morning comes.
```

Chorus 2

```
(G)                 Em      C       G
They are turn - ing my     head out,
   D                    Em
To see what I'm all a - bout.
              C           G
Keeping my    head down,
   D                        Em
To see what it feels like now.
      D              C
But I have no doubt,
     Am7          D                     (Em)
One      day the sun will come out.
```

Instr.

|: Em | Em | C | C |
| G/B | G/B | D | D :| *Play 4 times*

Outro

|: G | G | G | G :|

Lhuna

Words & Music by Guy Berryman, Chris Martin, Jon Buckland & Will Champion

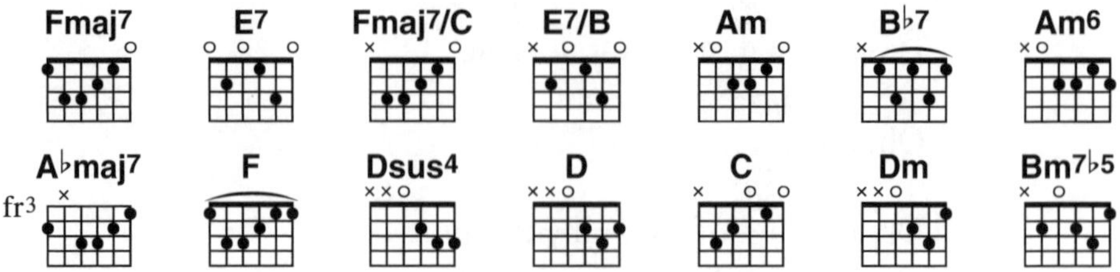

Capo first fret

Verse 2

Fmaj7 E7
I don't know what the time is,

Fmaj7 E7
I don't know where you've flown.

Fmaj7 E7 Fmaj7/C E7/B
And I don't know why you're so far from home.

Pre-chorus 2 As Pre-chorus 1

Chorus 2

(D) Am C
We are dreaming about Lhuna,

Dm Bm7♭5 B♭7
The smell of her, the touch and the taste of her.

Am C
Dreaming about Lhuna,

Bm7♭5 E7
Her and me simul - taneously,

Dsus4 B♭7
Her and me, effort - lessly,

Dsus4 B♭7
Oh, her and me effortlessly.

Outro

| Am | C | Dm | Dm Bm7♭5 B♭7 |

| Am | C | Bm7♭5 | E7 |

| Dsus4 | B♭7 | Dsus4 | B♭7 |

| Am | Am | Am | Am ‖

Verse 2

```
Fmaj7                      E7
   I don't know what the time is,
Fmaj7                           E7
   I don't know where you've flown.
Fmaj7                              E7            Fmaj7/C   E7/B
   And I don't know why you're so far from home.
```

Pre-chorus 2 As Pre-chorus 1

Chorus 2

```
(D)      Am                C
We are dreaming about Lhuna,
Dm                                        Bm7♭5   B♭7
   The smell of her, the touch and the taste of her.
Am                C
Dreaming about Lhuna,
Bm7♭5                     E7
Her and me simul - taneously,
Dsus4                      B♭7
Her and me, effort - lessly,
     Dsus4         B♭7
Oh, her and me effortlessly.
```

Outro

```
| Am      | C       | Dm      | Dm  Bm7♭5  B♭7 |
| Am      | C       | Bm7♭5   | E7      |
| Dsus4   | B♭7     | Dsus4   | B♭7     |
| Am      | Am      | Am      | Am      ||
```

A Message

Words & Music by Guy Berryman, Chris Martin, Jon Buckland & Will Champion

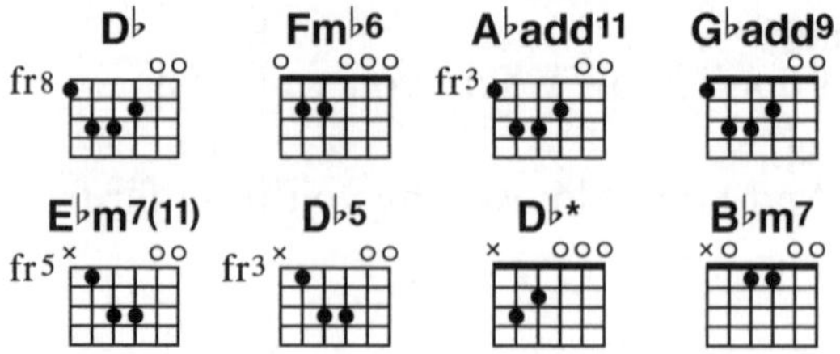

Tune guitar (from bottom string): F, B♭, E♭, A♭, A♭, D♭

Verse 1

D♭ Fm♭6 A♭add11
My song is love,
D♭ Fm♭6 A♭add11
Love to the loveless shown
D♭ Fm♭6 A♭add11
And it goes up.

G♭add9 Fm♭6 A♭add11
You don't have— to be— a - lone.

Verse 2

D♭ Fm♭6 A♭add11
Your heavy heart
D♭ Fm♭6 A♭add11 G♭add9
Is made of stone
D♭ Fm♭6 A♭add11
And it's so hard to see clearly.

G♭add9 Fm♭6 A♭add11
You don't have to be on your own,
G♭add9 Fm♭6 A♭add11
You don't have to be on your own.

Chorus 1

E♭m7(11) D♭5 A♭add11
And I'm not going to take it back,
E♭m7(11) D♭5 A♭add11
I'm not going to say I don't mean that,
E♭m7(11) D♭5 A♭add11
You're the target that I'm aiming at,
G♭add9 D♭* A♭add11
And I'll get that mess - age home.

Verse 3

D♭ Fm♭6 A♭add11
My song is love,
D♭ Fm♭6 A♭add11 G♭add9
My song is love un - known
D♭ Fm♭6 A♭add11
And I'm on fire for you, clearly.

G♭add9 Fm♭6 A♭add11
You don't have___ to be___ a - lone.
G♭add9 Fm♭6 A♭add11
You don't have___ to be on your own.

Chorus 2

E♭m7(11) D♭5 A♭add11
And I'm not going to take it back,
E♭m7(11) D♭5 A♭add11
I'm not going to say I don't mean that,
E♭m7(11) D♭5 A♭add11
You're the target that I'm aiming at
G♭add9 D♭* A♭add11
And I'm nothing___ on my own,
G♭add9 D♭* A♭add11
Got to get that mes - sage home.

Instrumental 1 ‖: E♭m7(11) | E♭m7(11) | D♭5 | A♭add11 :‖

Chorus 3

E♭m7(11) D♭5 A♭add11
And I'm not going to stand and wait,
E♭m7(11) D♭5 A♭add11
Not going to leave it until it's much too late,
E♭m7(11) D♭5 A♭add11
On a platform I'm going to stand and say
G♭add9 D♭* A♭add11
That I'm nothing___ on my own,
G♭add9 D♭* A♭add11
And I love you, please come home.

Instrumental 2 ‖: G♭add9 | D♭* | A♭add11 | B♭m7 :‖

Outro

G♭add9 D♭* A♭add11 B♭m7
But my song is love, is love unknown
G♭add9 D♭* A♭add11 D♭*
And I've got to get___ that message home.

Moses

Words & Music by Guy Berryman, Chris Martin, Jon Buckland & Will Champion

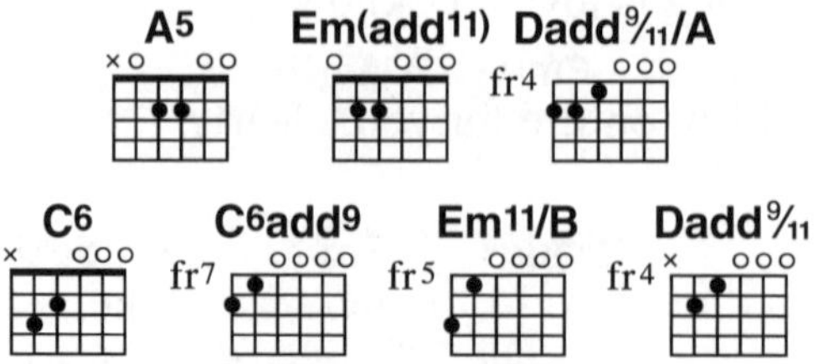

Capo second fret

Tune guitar (from bottom string): E, A, D, G, A, E

Intro ‖: A5 | Em(add11) | Em(add11) | Dadd9/11/A :‖ *Play 4 times*

Verse 1

A5 Em(add11)
Come on now
Dadd9/11/A
Don't you wanna see
A5 Em(add11)
This thing that's
Dadd9/11/A
Happening to me?
A5 Em(add11)
Like Moses
Dadd9/11/A
Has power over sea
A5 Em(add11)
So you've got
Dadd9/11/A
A power over me.

Instrumental 1 ‖: A5 | Em(add11) | Em(add11) | Dadd9/11/A :‖ *Play 4 times*

Verse 2

```
A5          Em(add11)
   Come  on  now
                       Dadd9/11/A
Don't you want to know
A5                Em(add11)
   That you're a refuge,
                      Dadd9/11/A
Somewhere I can go.
A5             Em(add11)
And you're air that,
                 Dadd9/11/A
Air that I can breathe.
A5               Em(add11)
   You're my golden
               Dadd9/11/A
Opportuni - ty.
```

Pre-chorus 1

```
      C6
And oh,
    C6add9  Em11/B         Dadd9/11
Oh, yes       I              would
          C6
If I only could.
           C6add9  Em11/B          Dadd9/11
Then you know     I                would.
```

Chorus 1

```
              C6  Dadd9/11
Now baby I
             C6  Dadd9/11
Oh, baby I.
```

Instrumental 2 ‖: A5 | Em(add11) | Em(add11) | Dadd9/11/A :‖

Verse 3

A5 Em(add11)
Come on now
Dadd9/11/A
Don't you wanna see
A5 Em(add11)
That just what a difference
Dadd9/11/A
You have made to me.
A5 Em(add11)
And I'll be waiting
Dadd9/11/A
No matter what you say
A5 Em(add11)
I'll keep waiting
Dadd9/11/A
For days and days and days.

Pre-chorus 2

C6
And oh,
C6add9 Em11/B Dadd9/11
Oh, yes I would
C6
If I only could.
C6add9 Em11/B Dadd9/11
And you know I would.

Chorus 2

C6 Dadd9/11
And baby I
C6 Dadd9/11
Oh baby I wish.

Bridge

|: A5 | Em(add11) | Em(add11) | Dadd9/11/A :| *Play 4 times w/vocal ad libs.*

C6 Dadd9/11 C6
If the skies go and fall down let it fall on me
Dadd9/11 C6
If you're caught in a break-down you can break on me
Dadd9/11 C6
If the sky's gonna fall down let it fall on me.
Dadd9/11
Oh Lord, let it fall on me.

Outro

|: A5 | Em(add11) | Em(add11) | Dadd9/11/A :| *Play 3 times*

| C6 | Dadd9/11 | Em(add11) ||

Murder

Words & Music by Guy Berryman, Chris Martin, Jon Buckland & Will Champion

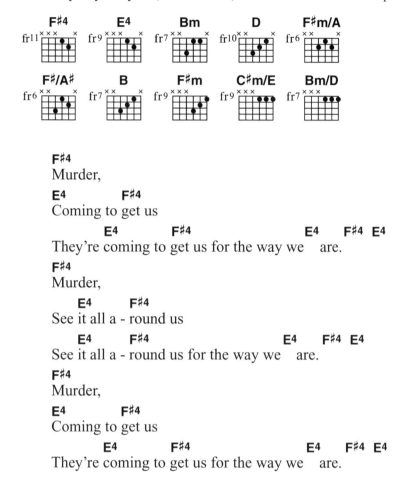

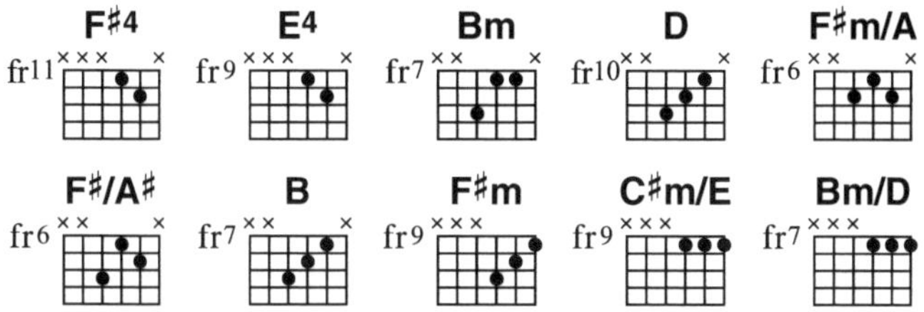

Intro

```
F#4
Murder,
E4            F#4
Coming to get us
           E4          F#4                          E4      F#4  E4
They're coming to get us for the way we    are.
F#4
Murder,
    E4          F#4
See it all a - round us
    E4          F#4                          E4      F#4  E4
See it all a - round us for the way we    are.
F#4
Murder,
E4            F#4
Coming to get us
           E4          F#4                          E4      F#4  E4
They're coming to get us for the way we    are.
```

Link 1

```
| Bm  D  | F#m/A  F#/A# | Bm  D  | F#m/A  F#/A# |
| Bm  D  | F#m/A  F#/A# | B  F#/A# | F#m/A      ||
```

Verse 1

```
Bm          D         F#m/A F#/A#
   Tie me to a tree
Bm          D                   F#m/A  F#/A#
   Tie my hands above my head.
Bm         D            F#m/A  F#/A#
   Sing a song to me
Bm         D                       F#m/A  F#/A#
   Sing a song like what you said.
```

Link 2 | Bm D | F♯m/A F♯/A♯ | Bm D | F♯m/A F♯/A♯ ||

Oh...

Chorus 1

Bm D F♯m/A F♯/A♯
They're gonna murder me
Bm D F♯m/A F♯/A♯
They're gonna track me down.
Bm D F♯m/A F♯/A♯
And even be - fore I sleep
B F♯/A♯ F♯m/A
I cry mur - der.

Link 3 | F♯4 E4 | F♯4 E4 | F♯4 E4 | F♯4 E4 ||

Verse 2

Bm D F♯m/A F♯/A♯
Come spit at us
Bm D F♯m/A F♯/A♯
Come and throw your weight a - round.
Bm D F♯m/A F♯/A♯
Come and fight with us
Bm D F♯m/A F♯/A♯
Try and knock us to the ground.

Chorus 2

Bm D F♯m/A F♯/A♯
They're gonna murder me
Bm D F♯m/A F♯/A♯
They're gonna track me down.
Bm D F♯m/A F♯/A♯
And even be - fore I sleep
B F♯m/A F♯/A♯
I scream mur - der.

Bridge

F♯m C♯m/E Bm/D F♯m C♯m/E Bm/D
Murder...
F♯m C♯m/E Bm/D
Oh, now what can it possibly gain.
F♯m C♯m/E Bm/D
Oh, what could it possibly gain.
F♯m C♯m/E Bm/D
Oh, what could it possibly gain.
F♯m C♯m/E Bm/D
Oh, yeah what could it possibly gain.

Link 4 | Bm D | F♯m/A F♯/A♯ | Bm D | F♯m/A F♯/A♯ |

w/vocal ad libs.

| Bm D | F♯m/A F♯/A♯ | F♯m/A | F♯m/A ||

Outro | F♯4 E4 | F♯4 E4 | F♯4 E4 | F♯4 E4 |

```
F♯4
Murder,
E4            F♯4
Coming to get us
          E4           F♯4                        E4     F♯4  E4
They're coming to get us for the way we   are.
F♯4
Murder,
    E4        F♯4
See it all a - round us
    E4        F♯4                        E4     F♯4  E4
See it all a - round us for the way we   are.
F♯4
Murder,
E4            F♯4
Coming to get us
          E4           F♯4                        E4     F♯4  E4
They're coming to get us for the way we   are.
F♯4
Murder,
N.C.
See it all around you.

See it all around you and the way we are.
```

No More Keeping My Feet On The Ground

Words & Music by Guy Berryman, Chris Martin, Jon Buckland & Will Champion

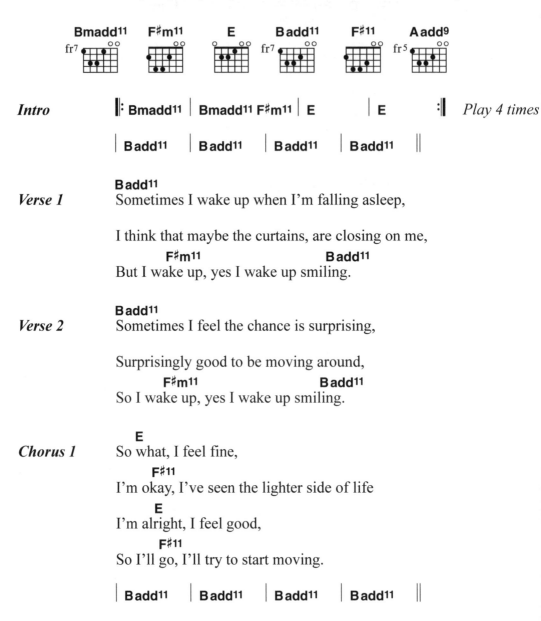

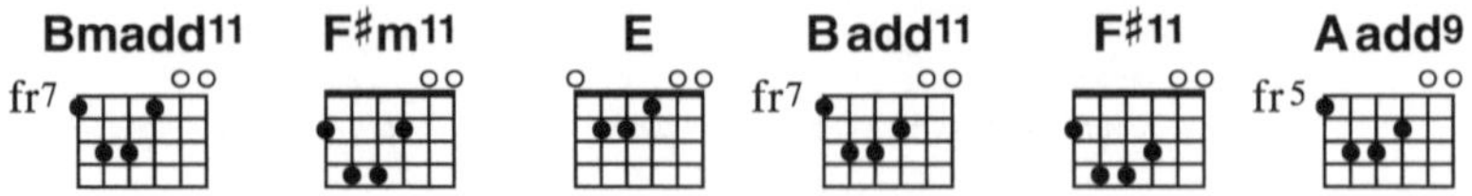

Intro |: Bmadd11 | Bmadd11 F♯m11 | E | E :| *Play 4 times*

| Badd11 | Badd11 | Badd11 | Badd11 ||

Verse 1

Badd11
Sometimes I wake up when I'm falling asleep,

I think that maybe the curtains, are closing on me,

F♯m11 Badd11
But I wake up, yes I wake up smiling.

Verse 2

Badd11
Sometimes I feel the chance is surprising,

Surprisingly good to be moving around,

F♯m11 Badd11
So I wake up, yes I wake up smiling.

Chorus 1

E
So what, I feel fine,

F♯11
I'm okay, I've seen the lighter side of life

E
I'm alright, I feel good,

F♯11
So I'll go, I'll try to start moving.

| Badd11 | Badd11 | Badd11 | Badd11 ||

Verse 3

Badd11
Sometimes I wake up and I'm falling asleep,
F♯m11
But I've got to get going, so much that I wanted to do,
Badd11 Aadd9
But I wake up smiling.

Bridge 1

F♯11
And this could be my last chance,
Aadd9
Of saving my innocence,
F♯11
And this could be my last chance,
Badd11
No more keeping my feet on the ground.

| Badd11 | Badd11 | Badd11 ||

Verse 4

Badd11
Sometimes I feel the chance is surprising,

Surprisingly good to be moving around,
F♯m11 Badd11
And I move, and I wake up smiling.

Chorus 2

E
So what, I feel fine,
F♯11
I feel okay, I've seen the lighter side of life
E
I'm alright, I feel good,
F♯11 Aadd9
So I'll go, well it's time to start moving.

Bridge 2

As Bridge 1

Outro

Badd11
And there's nothing to keep them,

There's nothing to keep them down

And there's nothing to keep them,

There's nothing to keep them down.

| Badd11 | Badd11 ||

Now My Feet Won't Touch The Ground

Words & Music by Guy Berryman, Chris Martin, Jon Buckland & Will Champion

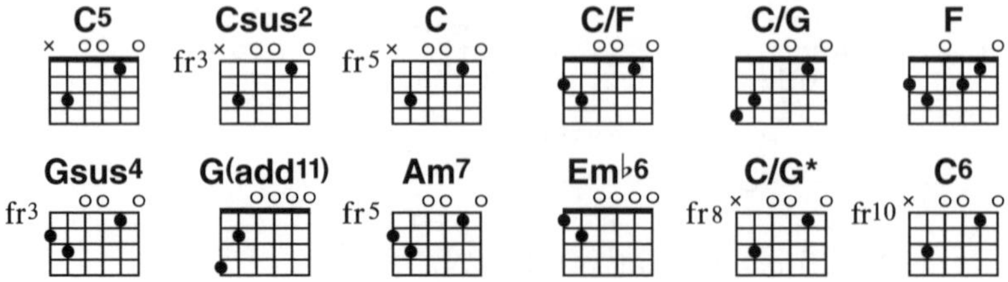

Tune guitar, (from bottom string): E♭, A, C, G, B, C

```
Intro      | C5  Csus2  | C5  Csus2  | C/F  C/G  | C5       ||

           (C5)                     F    C5
Verse 1    Let me go boys, let me go,
                                                        Gsus4   G(add11)
           Push my boat from the highest cliff to the sea be - low.
                  C5                          F
           Rocks are waiting boys, if rocks a - wait,
                 Am7             Em♭6   C/F               Gsus4  C5
           Swoop down from the sky and catch me like a bird of prey.

           (C5)  Csus2  C    Csus2  F          C5
Chorus 1   Now my       feet won't  touch the ground,
                 Csus2  C    C/G*  Gsus4  G(add11)
           Now my       head won't stop.
                    C5  Gsus4         C5
           You wait a   lifetime to be found,
                 Csus2  C    Csus2  F          C5
           Now my       feet won't  touch the ground.
```

Instr.

| (C5) Csus2 | C C/G* | C/G* C6 C/G* | Gsus4 F/C |

| C5 Csus2 | C C/G* | C/G* C6 C/G* Gsus4 | C/G* C Gsus4 |

| G(add11) | C/G* C6 C/G* C | C Gsus4 | F/C F |

| Am7 Em♭6 | C/F Gsus4 | C5 | C5 ||

Chorus 2

```
(C5)                Csus2  C     Csus2  F      C/G      C5
Singing now my            feet won't  touch      the ground,
            Csus2  C/G*  Gsus4  G(add11)
Now my head      won't stop.
            C5  Gsus4          C5
You wait a    lifetime to be found,
       Csus2  C    Csus2  F   C/G     C5
Now my        feet won't  touch the ground.
       Csus2  C    Csus2  F   C/G     C5
Now my        feet won't  touch the ground.
```

One I Love

Words & Music by Guy Berryman, Chris Martin, Jon Buckland & Will Champion

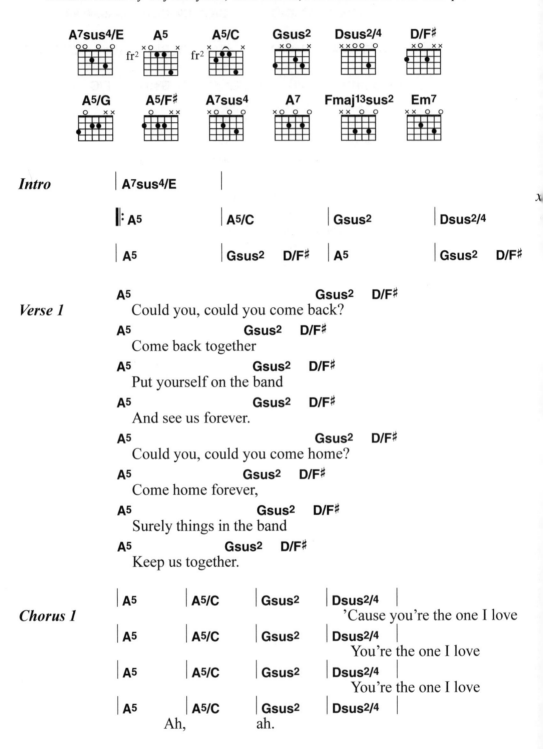

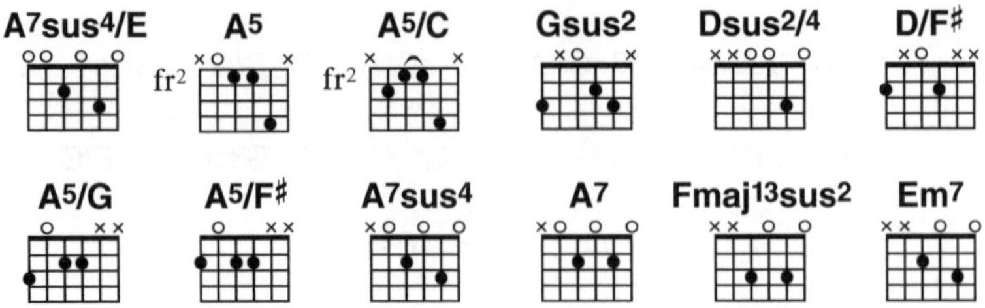

Intro

| A7sus4/E | |

‖: A5 | A5/C | Gsus2 | Dsus2/4 |

| A5 | Gsus2 D/F♯ | A5 | Gsus2 D/F♯ |

Verse 1

A5 Gsus2 D/F♯
Could you, could you come back?
A5 Gsus2 D/F♯
Come back together
A5 Gsus2 D/F♯
Put yourself on the band
A5 Gsus2 D/F♯
And see us forever.
A5 Gsus2 D/F♯
Could you, could you come home?
A5 Gsus2 D/F♯
Come home forever,
A5 Gsus2 D/F♯
Surely things in the band
A5 Gsus2 D/F♯
Keep us together.

Chorus 1

| A5 | A5/C | Gsus2 | Dsus2/4 |
'Cause you're the one I love
| A5 | A5/C | Gsus2 | Dsus2/4 |
You're the one I love
| A5 | A5/C | Gsus2 | Dsus2/4 |
You're the one I love
| A5 | A5/C | Gsus2 | Dsus2/4 |
Ah, ah.

Link 1 | ‖: A5 | A5/C | Gsus2 | Dsus2/4 :‖ x2

Verse 2

A5 Gsus2 D/F♯
Could you, could you come in?
A5 Gsus2 D/F♯
Could you tell me wherever?
A5 Gsus2 D/F♯
Tie yourself to a mast
A5 Gsus2 D/F♯
It's now or it's never.
A5 Gsus2 D/F♯
Could it tear us apart?
A5 Gsus2 D/F♯
It'll soon be forever
A5 Gsus2 D/F♯
It's gonna tear us apart
A5 Gsus2 D/F♯
Keep us together.

Chorus 2

| A5 | A5/C | Gsus2 | Dsus2/4 |
You're the one I love
| A5 | A5/C | Gsus2 | Dsus2/4 |
You're the one I love
| A5 | A5/C | Gsus2 | Dsus2/4 |
Ah. Ah. You're the one I love
| A5 | A5/C | Gsus2 | Dsus2/4 |
The one I love.

Link 2

‖: A5 | A5 | A5 | A5 :‖
Oooooooooo
| A5 | A5 | A5/G | A5/F♯ |
Oooooooooo.

Outro

‖: A5 | A5/C | Gsus2 | Dsus2/4 :‖ x4
‖: A7sus4 | A7sus4 | A7 | A7 :‖ x2
‖: Fmaj13sus2 | Em7 | A7 | A7 :‖ x3
| Fmaj13sus2 | Em7 | A7 ‖

Only Superstition

Words & Music by Guy Berryman, Chris Martin, Jon Buckland & Will Champion

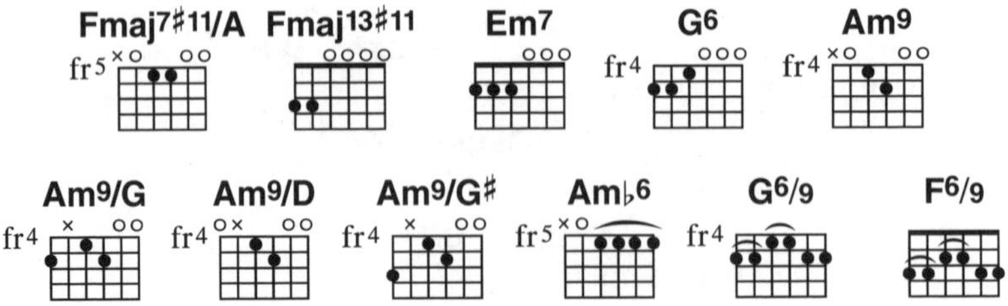

Tune guitar (from bottom string): D, A, C, G, B, E

Intro

| Fmaj7#11/A | Fmaj7#11/A |

‖: Fmaj13#11 Em7 Fmaj13#11 | G6 :‖ *Play 4 times*

Verse 1

```
Am9       Am9/G     Am9/D   Am9/G
   The cardboard head   I  see
Am9       Am9/G    Am9/D  Am9/G
   Has found its way to  me,
Am9  Am9/G      Am9/D       Am9/G
   It's out and it's out and it's out,
Am9          Am9/G   Am9/D    Am9/G
Making me cry.
Am9    Am9/G       Am9/D   Am9/G
   I    sleep but I will not move,
Am9        Am9/G    Am9/D    Am9/G
   I'm too scared to leave my room,
Am9        Am9/G    Am9/D          Am9/G  Am9  Am9/G  Am9/D  Am9/G
   But I won't be defeated, oh no.
```

Chorus 1

```
Fmaj13#11  G6                Fmaj13#11
   What if cars don't go my way
             G6           Fmaj13#11
And it's sure to spoil my day?
          G6           Fmaj13#11        G6
But in voices loud and clear you say to me:
```

cont.

Fmaj13#11 Em7 G6
"It's only superstition,

Em7 Fmaj13#11 G6 Fmaj13#11 Em7 G6
It's only your imagination,

Em7 Fmaj13#11 G6 Fmaj13#11 Em7
It's only all the things that you fear

Fmaj13#11 G6 Em7 Fmaj13#11 G6
And the things from which you can't escape."

| Fmaj13#11 Em7 Fmaj13#11 | G6 Em7 Fmaj13#11 G6 ||

Verse 2

Am9 Am9/G Am9/D Am9/G
Keep clean for the thousandth time,

Am9 Am9/G Am9/D Am9/G
Stand still and wait in line,

Am9 Am9/G Am9/D Am9/G
Some numbers are better than others,

Am9 Am9/G Am9/D Am9/G
Oh no.

Chorus 2

Fmaj13#11 G6 Fmaj13#11
What if cars don't go my way

G6 Fmaj13#11
And it's sure to spoil my day?

G6 Fmaj13#11 G6
But in voices loud and clear you say to me:

Fmaj13#11 Em7 G6
"It's only superstition,

Em7 Fmaj13#11 G6 Fmaj13#11 Em7 G6
It's only your imagination,

Em7 Fmaj13#11 G6 Fmaj13#11 Em7
It's only all of the things that you fear

Fmaj13#11 G6 Em7 Fmaj13#11 G6
And the things which you cannot ex - plain."

| Fmaj13#11 Em7 Fmaj13#11 | G6 Em7 Fmaj13#11 G6 ||

Bridge

Fmaj13#11 G6 Am9/G# Am9
And it's making me cry, and it's making me cry,

Fmaj13#11 G6 Am9/G# Am9
And I'm slipping away, and I'm slipping away.

Coda

Am♭6 G6/9 F6/9
It's only superstition, only your imagination,

Am♭6 G6/9 F6/9
It's only superstition, only superstition.

Parachutes

Words & Music by Guy Berryman, Chris Martin, Jon Buckland & Will Champion

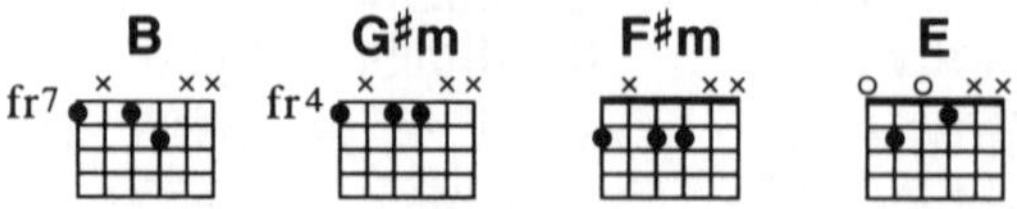

Tune guitar (from bottom string): E, A, B, G, B, D♯

Intro

| B | G♯m | B | G♯m |
| F♯m | F♯m | E | E ||

Verse 1

```
B
   In a haze,
   G♯m
A stormy haze,
B
   I'll be 'round,
         G♯m             F♯m
I'll be loving you always,
   E
Always
```

Verse 2

```
B
   Here I am
          G♯m
And I'll take my time.
B
   Here I am
          G♯m             F♯m
And I'll wait in line always,
   E
Always.
```

Postcards From Far Away

Words & Music by Guy Berryman, Chris Martin, Jon Buckland & Will Champion

Capo first fret

Instrumental				
	A	A	D	D
	A	A	D	D
	D	D	Ddim7	Ddim7
	C♯	C♯	F♯m	F♯m
	Bm	Bm	E7	E7
	Bm	Bm	F♯	F♯

Politik

Words & Music by Guy Berryman, Chris Martin, Jon Buckland & Will Champion

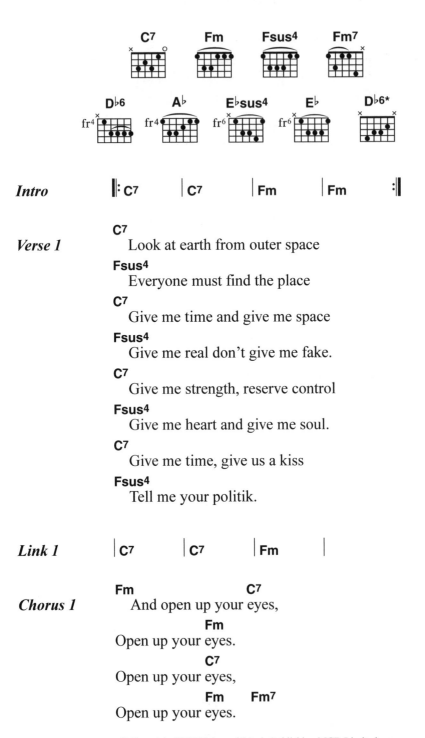

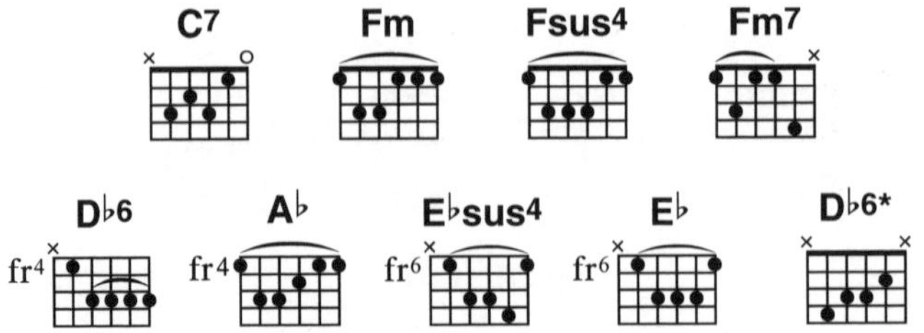

Intro ‖: C7 | C7 | Fm | Fm :‖

Verse 1

C7
Look at earth from outer space
Fsus4
Everyone must find the place
C7
Give me time and give me space
Fsus4
Give me real don't give me fake.
C7
Give me strength, reserve control
Fsus4
Give me heart and give me soul.
C7
Give me time, give us a kiss
Fsus4
Tell me your politik.

Link 1 | C7 | C7 | Fm |

Chorus 1

Fm C7
And open up your eyes,
Fm
Open up your eyes.
C7
Open up your eyes,
Fm Fm7
Open up your eyes.

Verse 2

```
C7
   Give me one, 'cause one is best,
Fsus4
   In confusion confidence
C7
   Give me peace of mind, and trust
Fsus4
   And don't forget the rest of us.
C7
   Give me strength, reserve control
Fsus4
   Give me heart and give me soul.
C7
   Wounds that heal, and cracks that fix
Fsus4
   Tell me your politik.
```

Chorus 2

```
                         C7
And open up your eyes,
                    Fm
Open up your eyes.
                    C7
Open up your eyes,
                    Fm
Open up your eyes.
      Fm7                C7
Just open up your (eyes.)
```

Link 2

```
| C7      | C7      | Fm      | Fm      | D♭6     |
  eyes.
| D♭6     | A♭      | A♭      | E♭sus4  | E♭      ||
```

Outro

```
Fm                          D♭6*                          A♭    E♭sus4  E♭   Fm
   Give me love over, love over, love over this.   Ah. ___________
                         D♭6*                         A♭          E♭sus4  E♭
Give me love over, love over, love over this.   Ah, ah ___________

| Fm      | Fm      | D♭6*    | D♭6*    | A♭      | A♭      |
| E♭sus4  | E♭      | Fm      | Fm      | D♭6*    | D♭6*    |
| A♭      | A♭      | E♭sus4  | E♭      | Fm (fermata) ||
```

Pour Me (Live)

Words & Music by Guy Berryman, Chris Martin, Jon Buckland & Will Champion

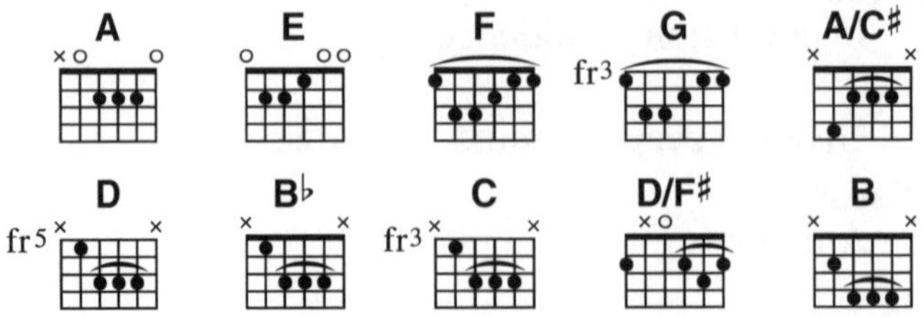

(Riff for 4 bars)

Intro ‖: A E | F A | F A | F G :‖

Verse 1

```
A       E  F                A
  Pour me flowing out to sea
   F          A           F  G
An opportu - nity that went by.
A       E       F              A
  Pour you now what you gonna do
    F               A          F  G
Now what you gonna do you just cry.
```

Link 1 | A E | F A | F A | F G ‖

Verse 2

```
A       E     F               A
  Pour me so blind I couldn't see
    F        A
The forest for the trees
          F  G
I don't know why.
A       E      F                 A
  Pour you, you split yourself in two
    F               A          F  G
Now what you gonna do you just cry.
```

Chorus 1

```
A/C♯ D          B♭       C
   I   hear you   come nearer
     D               D/F♯       F
   I hear you but I don't under - stand.
A/C♯ D          B♭       C
   I   hear you   come nearer
     D               D/F♯       F
   I hear you but I don't under - stand.
```

Link 2

```
| A  E  | F  A  | F  A  | F  G  ||
```

Verse 3

```
A       E  F              A
   Pour me flowing out to sea
   F          A              F   G
An opportu - nity that went by.
A       E          F              A
   Pour you now what you gonna do
   F                   A          F   G
Oh what you gonna do you just cry.
```

Chorus 2

```
A/C♯ D          B♭       C
   I   hear you   come nearer
     D               D/F♯       F
   I hear you but I don't under - stand.
A/C♯ D          B♭       C
   I   hear you   come nearer
     D               D/F♯       F
   I hear you but I don't under - stand.
```

Instrumental 1

```
||: C  D  | B              |
            I don't understand.
|   C  D  | B              |
            I don't understand.
|   C  D  | B            :||  Vocal ad libs. on repeat
```

Link 3

```
|  ———————— 8 ————————  ||
```

Guitar feedback + piano + vocal ad libs.

Outro

```
||: A/C♯ D | B♭  C | C  D | D/F♯  F :||
```

Vocal ad libs.

```
   A
|  ———————— 8 ————————  ||
```

Guitar feedback + piano

Proof

Words & Music by Guy Berryman, Chris Martin, Jon Buckland & Will Champion

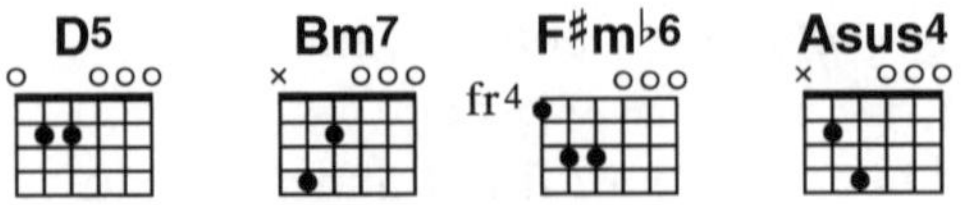

Capo second fret

Tune guitar (from bottom string): D, G, C, A, A, D

Intro | D5 | Bm7 | D5 | Bm7 ||

Verse 1

```
D5                    Bm7
   So I waited for you
F♯m♭6                  Bm7
   What wouldn't I do?
D5                          Bm7
   And I'm covered it's true
F♯m♭6               Bm7
   I'm covered in you.
D5                 Bm7
   If I ever want proof
F♯m♭6          Bm7
   I find it in you.
D5                    Bm7
   Yeah I honestly do
F♯m♭6             Bm7
   In you I find proof.
```

Chorus 1

```
Asus4         Bm7
   Light dark
F♯m♭6            Bm7
   Bright spark.
Asus4         Bm7
   Light dark    and then
F♯m♭6     Bm7
   Light.
```

Link 1 | D5 | Bm7 | D5 | Bm7 ||

Verse 2

```
D5                 Bm7
   So I waited all day
F♯m♭6                Bm7
   What wouldn't I say?
D5                          Bm7
   All the things in your way
F♯m♭6                    Bm7
   Things happen that way.
    D5                      Bm7
Oh,    and if I ever want proof
F♯m♭6                       Bm7
   Then I find it in you.
    D5                  Bm7
Oh,    yeah I honestly do
F♯m♭6              Bm7
   In you I find proof.
```

Chorus 2

```
Asus4          Bm7
   Light dark
F♯m♭6             Bm7
   Bright spark.
Asus4          Bm7
   Light dark      and then
F♯m♭6     Bm7
   Light.
```

Outro

```
|: D5     | Bm7    | D5     | Bm7    :|
            Light

 (fermata)
| D5      ||
```

Prospekt's March/ Poppyfields

Words & Music by Guy Berryman, Chris Martin, Jon Buckland & Will Champion

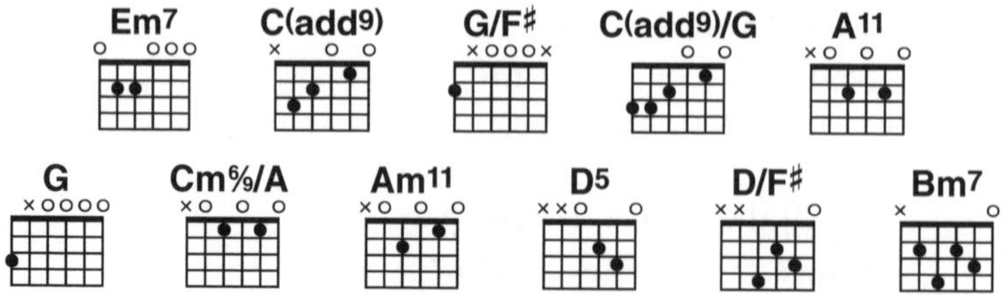

Tune first string to D
Capo seventh fret

Verse

Em7 C(add9)
Smoke is rising from the houses,
Em7 C(add9)
People burying their dead.
Em7 C(add9)
I ask somebody what the time is,
Em7 C(add9)
But time doesn't matter to them yet.
G/F♯ C(add9)/G Em7 G/F♯ C(add9)/G
People talking without speaking,
Em7 G/F♯ C(add9)/G
Trying to take what they can get.
Em7
I ask you if you re - member,
A11 C(add9)
Prospekt, how could I for - get?

Pre-chorus

```
G                 Em7
Drums, here it comes,
C(add9)
Don't you wish that life could be as simple

As fish swimming round in a barrel
       A11
When you've got the gun?
Cm6/9/A  G            Em7
Oh and I run, here it comes,
            C(add9)/G
We're just two little figures in a soup bowl

Trying to get the other kind of control,
    Am11    C(add9)
But I wasn't one.
```

Chorus

```
             D5  D/F#       Bm7                C(add9)
But here I lie___ on my own in a separate sky,
             D5  D/F#       Bm7                C(add9)
And here I lie___ on my own in a separate sky.
                D5  D/F#      Bm7          C(add9)
I don't wanna die___ on my own here to - night,
             D5  D/F#       Bm7                C(add9)  G
But here I lie___ on my own in a separate sky.
```

Outro

```
||: G      | G      | Em7    | D5     :||
```

Play 3 times to fade

Rainy Day

Words & Music by Guy Berryman, Chris Martin, Jon Buckland & Will Champion

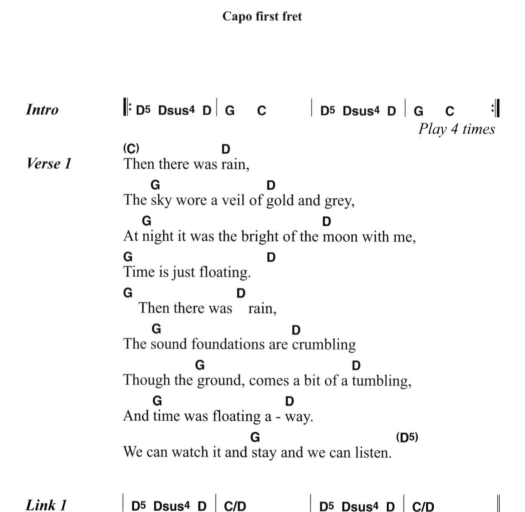

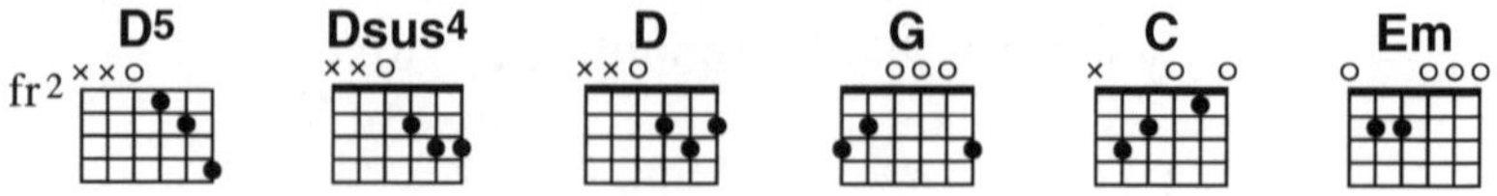

Capo first fret

```
Intro      |: D5 Dsus4 D | G    C     | D5 Dsus4 D | G    C    :|
                                                     Play 4 times

           (C)             D
Verse 1    Then there was rain,
               G                   D
           The sky wore a veil of gold and grey,
             G                             D
           At night it was the bright of the moon with me,
           G                   D
           Time is just floating.
           G              D
             Then there was  rain,
               G                        D
           The sound foundations are crumbling
                          G                         D
           Though the ground, comes a bit of a tumbling,
               G                  D
           And time was floating a - way.
                                G                      (D5)
           We can watch it and stay and we can listen.

Link 1     | D5 Dsus4 D | C/D        | D5 Dsus4 D | C/D        ||
```

```
             C              G            D
Chorus 1       Oh, rainy day, come round,
             C                     G                  D
               Sometimes I just want it to slow down.
             C                   Em        D
               And we're sepa - rated now,    I'm down.
                 C                                 G
             But I love it when you come over to my house,
                                  D
             I love it when you come over to my house.


Link 2       ||: D5 Dsus4 D | G    C      | D5 Dsus4 D | G    C      :||


             (C)            D
Verse 2      Then there was rain,
             G                         D
             I spent the night with the Queen of Spain,
                 G                          D
             My lonely little heart would've broke again,
             G                  D  G
             Time is so vicious.        (Sing.)
                         D                         G                   D
             Singing, the deeper that the knife goes in, the more you win,
                                G
             You end up with less than when you begin.
                 D                        G      D  G
             The deeper that the knife goes in, oh.____


Chorus 2     As Chorus 1


                 C  G  D
Link         Ah,________
                 C  G  D
             Ah,________
                 C  Em  D
             Ah,________


             (D)  C                               G
Outro        But I love it when you come over to my house,
                                  D
             I love it when you come over to my house.
                 C                             G
             I love it when you come over to my house,
                                  D
             I love it when you come over to my house.
```

Reign Of Love

Words & Music by Guy Berryman, Chris Martin, Jon Buckland & Will Champion

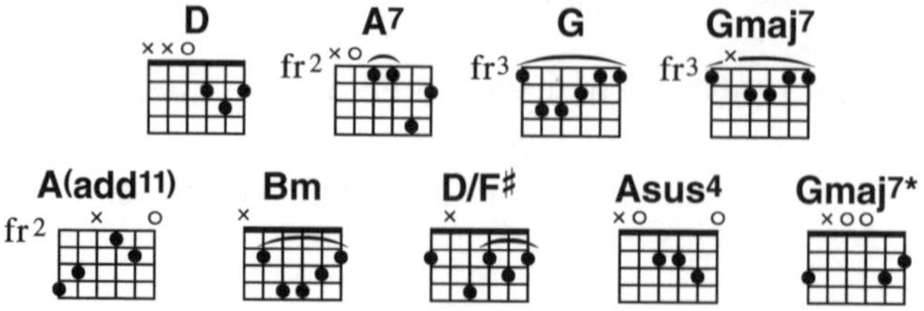

Intro |: D A7 | D | G Gmaj7 | A(add11) :|
| D A7 | D | Bm D/F♯ | G |
| G Asus4 | D | Gmaj7* Asus4 | D ||

Verse 1
D A7 D G Gmaj7 A(add11)
Reign of love, I can't let go.
D A7 D G Gmaj7 A(add11)
To the sea I of - fer this hea - vy load.
D A7 D Bm D/F♯ G
Lo - cust wind lift me up,
Asus4 D Gmaj7* Asus4 D
I'm just a prisoner in a reign of love.

Instr. 1 |: D A7 | D | G Gmaj7 | A(add11) :|

Verse 2
D A7 D Bm D/F♯ G
Lo - cust will let us stop,
Asus4 D Gmaj7* Asus4 D
How I wish I'd spoken up to a reign of love.

Verse 3

```
D           A7   D          G              Gmaj7    A(add11)
Reign of     love, by the church we're waiting.
D           A7   D          G          Gmaj7    A(add11)
Reign of     love, on my knees, go praying.
D       A7 D         Bm   D/F#  G
How I    wish I'd spo - ken   up,
     Asus4         D          Gmaj7* Asus4  D
A - way get car - ried on a reign   of       love.
```

Instr. 2

```
||: D    A7      | D          | G   Gmaj7       | A(add11)     :||
|   D    A7      | D          | Bm   D/F#       | G             |
|   G   Asus4    | D          | Gmaj7* Asus4    | D             ||
```

Low

Words & Music by Guy Berryman, Chris Martin, Jon Buckland & Will Champion

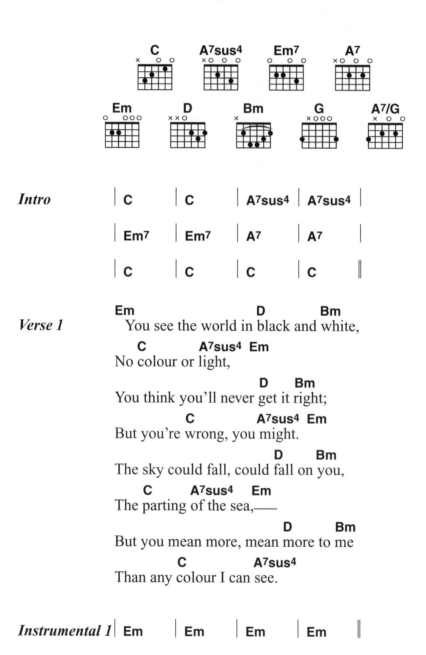

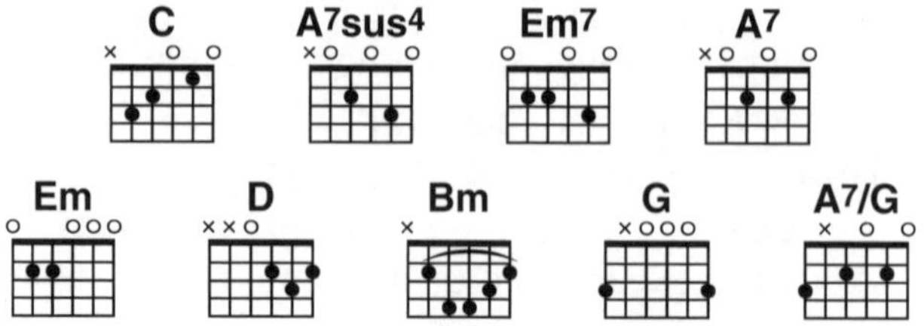


```
Intro          | C      | C      | A7sus4 | A7sus4 |
               | Em7    | Em7    | A7     | A7     |
               | C      | C      | C      | C      ||

                 Em                          D         Bm
Verse 1            You see the world in black and white,
                    C           A7sus4 Em
                 No colour or light,
                                              D      Bm
                 You think you'll never get it right;
                              C               A7sus4 Em
                 But you're wrong, you might.
                                                  D       Bm
                 The sky could fall, could fall on you,
                       C           A7sus4    Em
                 The parting of the sea,——
                                                     D         Bm
                 But you mean more, mean more to me
                                  C              A7sus4
                 Than any colour I can see.

Instrumental 1 | Em     | Em     | Em     | Em     ||
```

Chorus 1

```
C                                    A7sus4
   All you ever wanted was love
                                  Em7
But you never look hard enough,
                                    A7
It's never gonna give itself up.
C                                 A7sus4
   All you ever wanted to be,
                                   Em7
Living in perfect symme - try,
                                      A7     (C)
But nothing is as down or as up as us.
```

Instrumental 2

```
| C        | C        | C        | C        |
(us.)
| Em       | Em   D   | Bm       | Bm       |

| C        | A7sus4   | Em       | Em       ||
```

Verse 2

```
Em                            D          Bm
   You see the world in black and white,
     C         A7sus4  Em
Not painted right.
                              D        Bm
You see no meaning to your life,
                C    A7sus4    Em
You should try,_____________
                C    A7sus4    (Em)
You should try._____________
```

Instrumental 3

```
| Em       | Em       | Em       | Em       ||
```

```
             C                            A7sus4
Chorus 2       All you ever wanted was love
                                           Em7
             But you never look hard e - nough,
                                           A7
             It's never gonna give itself up.
             C                          A7sus4
               All you ever wanted to be,
                                          Em7
             Living in perfect symme - try
                                              A7
             But nothing is as down or as up,
             C                                     A7sus4
               Don't you want to see it come soon?
                                           Em7
             Floating in a big white bal - loon,
                                              A7
             Or flying on your own silver spoon.
             C                                     A7sus4
               Don't you want to see it come down,
                                                    Em7
             There for throwing your arms a - round
                                            A7
             Saying, "Not a moment too soon."

             G                 A7/G
Bridge         'Cause I feel low,
             G                 A7/G
               'Cause I feel low, oh...
             G         C          A7/G
             But I feel low, oh no.

Instrumental 4| G        | A7/G     | G        | A7/G     |

              | G        | Em7      | A7sus4   | A7sus4   ||

               G                A7/G
Outro        Oh, 'cause I feel low,
             G                  A7/G
                'Cause I feel low, oh,
             G         C          A7sus4
             But I feel low, oh no,
                 G
             Oh.___
```

A Rush Of Blood To The Head

Words & Music by Guy Berryman, Chris Martin, Jon Buckland & Will Champion

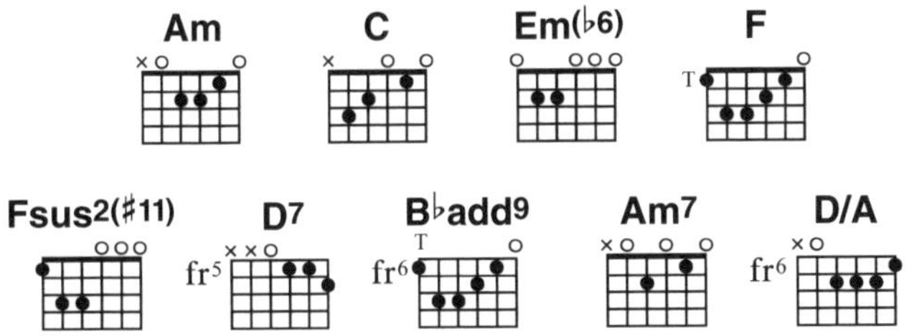

Tune guitar (from bottom string): E, A, D, G, B, C

Verse 1

```
              Am                                 C
He said I'm gonna buy this place and burn it down,
  Em(♭6)                          Am
I'm gonna put it six feet underground.
                                                C
He said I'm gonna buy this place and watch it fall
   Em(♭6)                                 Am
Stand here beside me baby in the crumbling walls.
```

Verse 2

```
        Am                                C
Oh I'm gonna buy this place and start a fire,
   Em(♭6)                            Am
Stand here until I fill all your heart's desires.
                                                 C
Because I'm gonna buy this place and see it burn
  Em(♭6)                            Am  | Am |
Do back the things it did to you in return.
```

Link 1

```
    F     Fsus2(♯11)
Ha _ ha __________
    F     Fsus2(♯11)
Ha _ ha.__________
```

Verse 3

```
              Am                                 C
He said I'm gonna buy a gun and start a war,
 Em(♭6)                                           Am
If you can tell me something worth fighting for.
                                                 C
Oh and I'm gonna buy this place, is what I say,
Em(♭6)                                   Am  | Am |
Blame it upon a rush of blood to the head.
```

Chorus 1

```
     F                                           D7
Honey, all the movements you're starting to make
                                 F
See me crumble and fall on my face.
                                      D7
And I know the mistakes that I've made,
         B♭add9                  F
See it all disappear without a trace,
                                 D7
And they call as they beckon you on,
              B♭add9                  (Am)
They said start as you mean to go on.
```

```
| Am      | C       | Em(♭6)   |
```

```
Am
  Start as you mean to go on.
```

```
| Am      | C       | Em(♭6)   | Am       |
```

Verse 4

```
             Am                                   C
He said I'm gonna buy this place and see it go,
   Em(♭6)                                          Am
Stand here beside my baby, watch the orange glow.
                                          C
Some will laugh and some just sit and cry,
        Em(♭6)                                     Am
But you just sit down there and you wonder why.
```

Verse 5

```
       Am                                C
So I'm gonna buy a gun and start a war,
Em(♭6)                                          Am
If you can tell me something worth fighting for.
                                               C
Oh and I'm gonna buy this place, is what I say,
Em(♭6)                                    Am
Blame it upon a rush of blood to the head, oh to the head.
```

Chorus 2

F D7
Honey, all the movements you're starting to make

F
See me crumble and fall on my face.

D7
And I know the mistakes that I've made,

B♭add9 F
See it all disappear without a trace,

D7
And they call as they beckon you on,

B♭add9 (Am)
They said start as you mean to go on.

Am C Em(♭6)
As you mean to go on,

Am
As you mean to go on.

| Am | C | Em(♭6) |

Verse 6

Am
So meet me by the bridge,

C
Oh meet me by the lake.

Em(♭6) Am
When am I gonna see that pretty face again?

Oh meet me on the road,

C
Oh meet me where I ___ said,

Em(♭6) Am7 D/A
Blame it all upon a rush of blood to the head.

Outro

| Am7 D/A | Am7 D/A | Am7 D/A | Am (fermata) ‖

The Scientist

Words & Music by Guy Berryman, Chris Martin, Jon Buckland & Will Champion

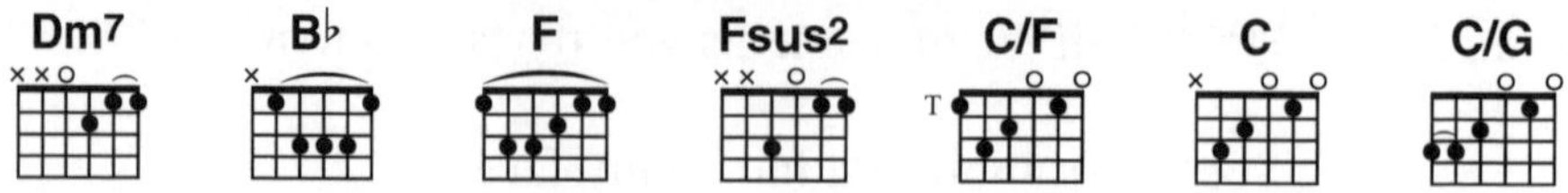

Intro |: Dm7 | B♭ | F | Fsus2 :|

Verse 1

Dm7 B♭
Come up to meet you,
F
Tell you I'm sorry,
Fsus2
You don't know how lovely you are.
Dm7 B♭
I had to find you,
F
Tell you I need you,
Fsus2 C/F
Tell you I'll set you apart.
Dm7 B♭
Tell me your secrets,
F
And ask me your questions,
Fsus2 C/F
Oh let's go back to the start.
Dm7 B♭
Running in circles,
F
Coming up tails,
Fsus2 C/F
Heads on a silence apart.

Chorus 1

B♭
Nobody said it was easy,
F Fsus2
It's such a shame for us to part.
B♭
Nobody said it was easy,
F C/F Fsus2 C
No-one ever said it would be this hard.
C/G (F)
Oh, take me back to the start.

Link | F | B♭ | F | F | F | B♭ | F | Fsus2 ||

Verse 2

Dm7 B♭
I was just guessing
F
At numbers and figures,
Fsus2
Pulling your puzzles apart.
Dm7 B♭
Questions of science,
F
Science and progress,
Fsus2
Do not speak as loud as my heart.
Dm7 B♭
Tell me you love me,
F
Come back and haunt me,
Fsus2
Oh and I rush to the start.
Dm7 B♭
Running in circles,
F
Chasing our tails,
Fsus2
Coming back as we are.

Chorus 2

B♭
Nobody said it was easy,
F Fsus2
Oh it's such a shame for us to part.
B♭
Nobody said it was easy,
F C/F Fsus2 C
No-one ever said it would be so hard.
C/G (F)
I'm going back to the start.

Instrumental | F | B♭ | F | F | Dm7 | B♭ | F | F ||

Outro

Dm7 B♭ F | F |
Ooh ________
Dm7 B♭ F | F |
Ah ooh ________
Dm7 B♭ F | F |
Oh ooh ________
Dm7 B♭ F (fermata)
Oh ooh.

See You Soon

Words & Music by Guy Berryman, Chris Martin, Jon Buckland & Will Champion

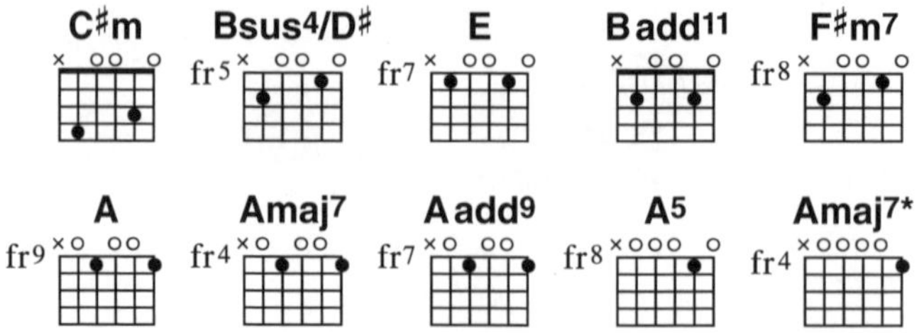

Tune guitar (from bottom string): F♯, G, D, D, B, D,
Capo second fret

Intro

```
| C♯m  Bsus4/D♯  E | Badd11     | C♯m  Bsus4/D♯  E | Badd11
| C♯m  Bsus4/D♯  E | Badd11     | F♯m7  E  | Badd11      ||
```

Verse 1

```
C♯m  Bsus4/D♯  E              Badd11
  So you       lost your trust,
                        C♯m
And you never shared her,
       Bsus4/D♯  E             Badd11
And you       never shared her.
C♯m    Bsus4/D♯  E               Badd11
  But don't      break your back,
                   C♯m   Bsus4/D♯   E           Badd11
If you ever see this,   don't       answer that.
```

Chorus 1

```
A        Amaj7  Aadd9  Amaj7
  In a bullet - proof  vest,
               Badd11      A
With the windows all closed,
          Amaj7  Aadd9  Amaj7           A5
I'll be doing   my      best, I'll see you soon
A        Amaj7   Aadd9   Amaj7
  In a tele   -  scope   lens.
                Badd11        A5      Amaj7*
And when all you want is friends,   I'll see you soon.
```

Link 1

```
| C♯m  Bsus4/D♯  E | Badd11     | C♯m  Bsus4/D♯  E | Badd11
```

Verse 2

```
C♯m  Bsus4/D♯   E          Badd11
   So they       came for you,
                                    C♯m
They came snapping at your heels,
      Bsus4/D♯   E                   Badd11
They come        snapping at your    heels.
C♯m   Bsus4/D♯   E           Badd11
   But don't     break your back,
                  C♯m
If you ever say this,
     Bsus4/D♯   E         Badd11
But don't       answer that.
```

Chorus 2

```
A       Amaj7  Aadd9  Amaj7
   In a bullet - proof  vest,
            Badd11        A
With the windows all closed,
        Amaj7  Aadd9  Amaj7              A5
I'll be doing   my     best, I'll see you soon
A       Amaj7  Aadd9   Amaj7
   In a tele  -  scope   lens.
      Badd11                  A5        Amaj7*
And when all you want is friends,   I'll see you soon.
```

Link 2

```
| C♯m  Bsus4/D♯  E | Badd11 | C♯m  Bsus4/D♯  E | Badd11            |
                                                 I'll see you soon.

| C♯m  Bsus4/D♯  E | Badd11 | C♯m  Bsus4/D♯  E | Badd11      ||
```

Coda

```
  A5          E            Badd11
I know you lost your trust,
  A5          E            Badd11
I know you lost your trust,
  A5             E            Badd11
I know, don't lose your trust,
  A5          E         Badd11
I know you lost your trust.
```

Shiver

Words & Music by Guy Berryman, Chris Martin, Jon Buckland & Will Champion

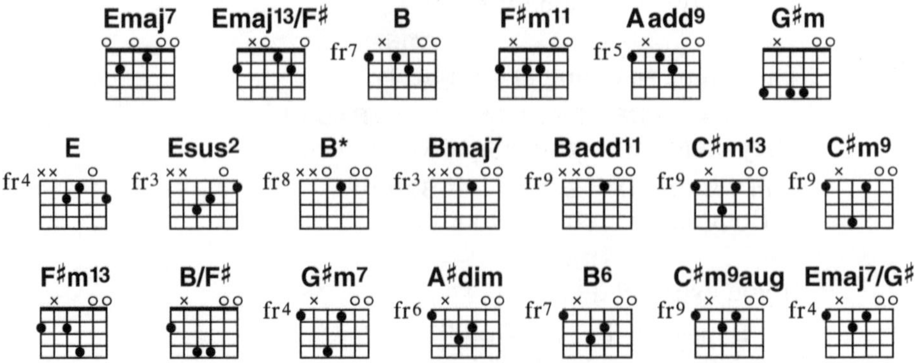

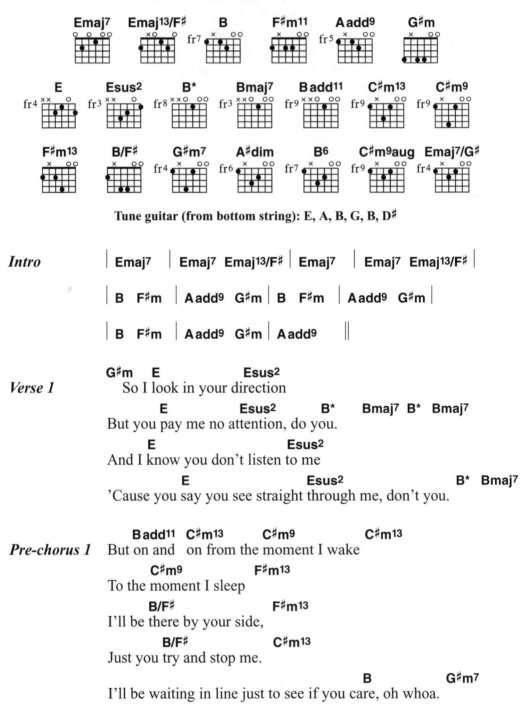

Tune guitar (from bottom string): E, A, B, G, B, D♯

Intro

Emaj7	Emaj7 Emaj13/F♯	Emaj7	Emaj7 Emaj13/F♯
B F♯m	Aadd9 G♯m	B F♯m	Aadd9 G♯m
B F♯m	Aadd9 G♯m	Aadd9	

Verse 1

G♯m E Esus2
So I look in your direction
E Esus2 B* Bmaj7 B* Bmaj7
But you pay me no attention, do you.
E Esus2
And I know you don't listen to me
E Esus2 B* Bmaj7 E
'Cause you say you see straight through me, don't you.

Pre-chorus 1

Badd11 C♯m13 C♯m9 C♯m13
But on and on from the moment I wake
C♯m9 F♯m13
To the moment I sleep
B/F♯ F♯m13
I'll be there by your side,
B/F♯ C♯m13
Just you try and stop me.
B G♯m7
I'll be waiting in line just to see if you care, oh whoa.

cont.

A#dim B6
Did you want me to change?

A#dim G#m7
Well I'd change for good.

A#dim B6
And I want you to know

C#m9aug B6
That you'll always get your way.

A#dim G#m7 Emaj7/G#
I wanted to say:

Chorus 1

B F#m11 Aadd9 G#m
Don't you shiver,

B6 F#m11 Aadd9 G#m
Shiver,

B Aadd9 G#m7
Shiver, ooh. ______

Aadd9 G#m
I'll always be waiting for you.

Verse 2

E Esus2
So you know how much I need you

E Esus2 B* Bmaj7 B* Bmaj7
But you never even see me, do you?

E Esus2 E Esus2 B* Bmaj7 B*
And is this my final chance of getting you?

Pre-chorus 2

Badd11 C#m13 C#m9 C#m13
But on and on from the moment I wake

C#m9 F#m13
To the moment I sleep

B/F# F#m13
I'll be there by your side,

B/F# C#m13
Just you try and stop me.

B G#m7
I'll be waiting in line just to see if you care, oh whoa.

A#dim B6
Did you want me to change?

A#dim G#m7
Well I'd change for good.

A#dim B6
And I want you to know

C#m9aug B6
That you'll always get your way.

A#dim G#m7 Emaj7/G#
I wanted to say:

Chorus 2

```
                        B  F#m11  Aadd9  G#m
Don't you shiver,
        B6  F#m11  Aadd9  G#m
Shiver,
        B   Aadd9     G#m7
Shiver,     ooh. ____
    Aadd9                    G#m
I'll always be waiting for you.

| Emaj7     | Emaj7     | Emaj7     ||
```

Bridge

```
            B          Aadd9           Emaj7
Yeah, I'll always be waiting for you,
            B          Aadd9           Emaj7
Yeah, I'll always be waiting for you,
            B          Aadd9           Emaj7
Yeah, I'll always be waiting for you,

For you, I will always be waiting.
          B     F#m11       Aadd9         G#m
And it's you I see but you don't see me,
          B     F#m11  Aadd9             G#m
And it's you I hear so loud and clear.
          B   F#m11  Aadd9   G#m
I sing it loud ___ and clear
          Aadd9                  G#m
And I'll always be waiting for you.
```

Verse 3

```
     Emaj7           Esus2
So I look in your direction
          Emaj7        Esus2
But you pay me no attention.
           Emaj7               Esus2
And you know how much I need you
          Emaj7       Esus2
But you never even see me.
```

Sleeping Sun

Words & Music by Guy Berryman, Chris Martin, Jon Buckland & Will Champion

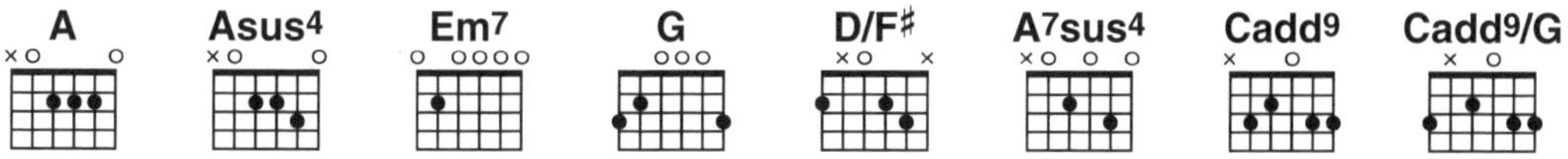

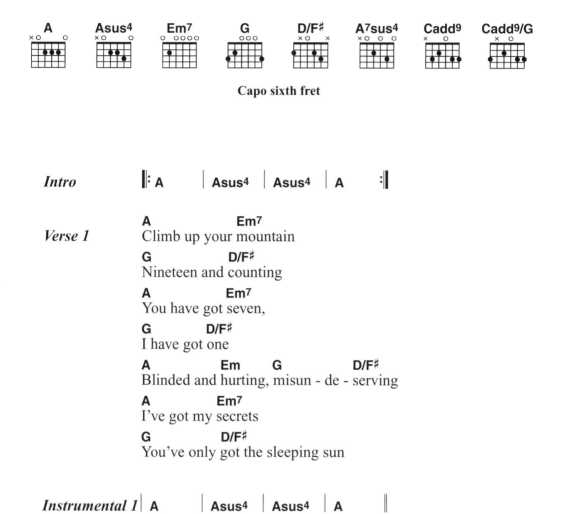

Capo sixth fret

Intro ‖: A | Asus4 | Asus4 | A :‖

Verse 1

```
A                  Em7
Climb up your mountain
G                D/F♯
Nineteen and counting
A                Em7
You have got seven,
G             D/F♯
I have got one
A              Em        G               D/F♯
Blinded and hurting, misun - de - serving
A               Em7
I've got my secrets
G              D/F♯
You've only got the sleeping sun
```

Instrumental 1 | A | Asus4 | Asus4 | A ‖

Verse 2

```
A                    Em7
When you've got a secret
G                    D/F#
Then you've got to keep it
A                    Em7
When you've got a question
G              D/F#
Answers will come
A              Em
Running and hiding
G              D/F#
Take and di - viding
A                 Em7
You've got your secrets
G          D/F#
I've only got a sleeping sun
```

Instrumental 2 ‖: A | Asus4 | Asus4 | A :‖

Chorus 1

```
         A     A7sus4
Singing, ooh, ooh, ooh
A     A7sus4
Ooh, ooh, ooh
A     A7sus4
Ooh, ooh, ooh
A     A7sus4
Ooh, ooh, ooh
A   A7sus4
Ah, ah, ah
A   A7sus4
Oh, oh, oh
A   A7sus4
Ah, ah, ah
A   A7sus4
Oh, oh, oh
```

Instrumental 3 | A | A | A | A ‖

Verse 3

```
A                Em7
And you, as I saw
G                D/F♯
A piece in a jigsaw
A                    Em7
Run up and a - round it
       G                 D/F♯
And jump up real tall
A                   Em
Run round the houses
G                   D/F♯
North and the souths'
A                      Em7
You've got your answers
G                  D/F♯
We have both got a sleeping sun
```

Instrumental 4 ||: A | Asus4 | Asus4 | A :||

Chorus 2

```
              A      A7sus4
Singing, ooh, ooh, ooh
A       A7sus4
Ooh, ooh, ooh
A       A7sus4
Ooh, ooh, ooh
A       A7sus4
Ooh, ooh, ooh
A     A7sus4
Ah, ah, ah
A     A7sus4
Oh, oh, oh
A     A7sus4
Ah, ah, ah
A     A7sus4
Oh, oh, oh
```

Instrumental 5 | A | A | A | A ||

||: A | A | Cadd9 | Cadd9/G :||

| A7sus4 ||

Sparks

Words & Music by Guy Berryman, Chris Martin, Jon Buckland & Will Champion

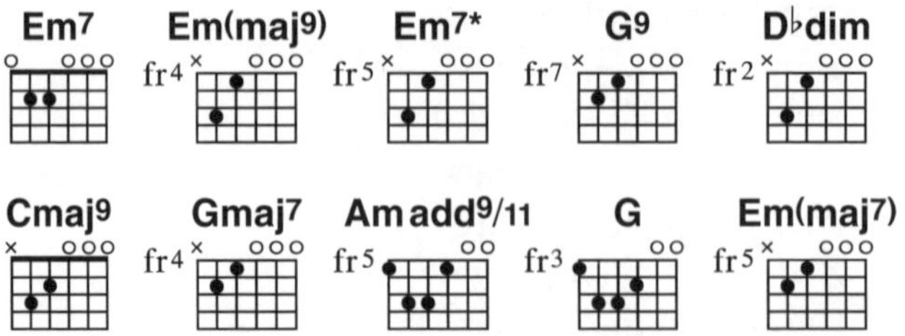

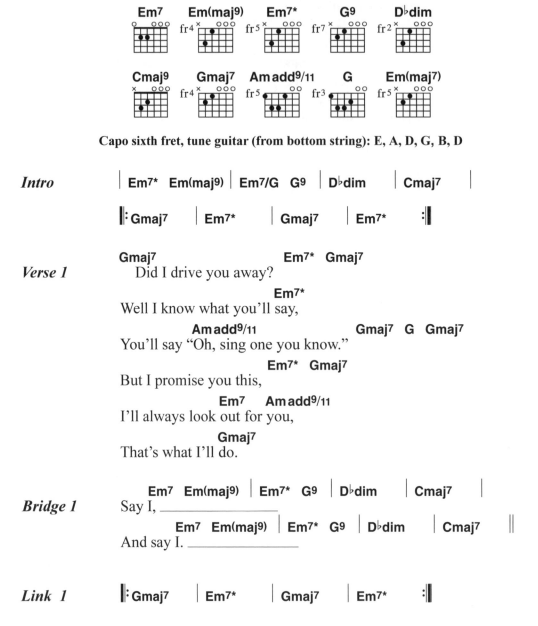

Capo sixth fret, tune guitar (from bottom string): E, A, D, G, B, D

Intro
| **Em7* Em(maj9)** | **Em7/G G9** | **D♭dim** | **Cmaj7** |

𝄆 **Gmaj7** | **Em7*** | **Gmaj7** | **Em7*** 𝄇

Verse 1

Gmaj7 Em7* Gmaj7
Did I drive you away?
Em7*
Well I know what you'll say,
Am add9/11 Gmaj7 G Gmaj7
You'll say "Oh, sing one you know."
Em7* Gmaj7
But I promise you this,
Em7 Am add9/11
I'll always look out for you,
Gmaj7
That's what I'll do.

Bridge 1

Em7 Em(maj9) | **Em7* G9** | **D♭dim** | **Cmaj7** |
Say I, _______________
Em7 Em(maj9) | **Em7* G9** | **D♭dim** | **Cmaj7** ||
And say I. _______________

Link 1
𝄆 **Gmaj7** | **Em7*** | **Gmaj7** | **Em7*** 𝄇

Verse 2

```
Gmaj7                    Em7*  Gmaj7
   My heart is yours,
                 Em7*    Amadd9/11
It's you that I hold on to,
                 Gmaj7  G  Gmaj7
That's what I do.
                                 Em7*  Em(maj7)  Gmaj7
And I know I was wrong,
                     Em7
But I won't let you down.
Amadd9/11                                 Gmaj7  G
Oh yeah, I will, yeah I will, yes I will.
```

Bridge 2

```
      Em7  Em(maj9) | Em7*  G9 | D♭dim    | Cmaj7    |
I said I, ________________
      Em7  Em(maj9) | Em7*  G9 | D♭dim    | Cmaj7    ||
I cry I. ________________
```

Chorus

```
           Gmaj7   Em7*
And I saw sparks,
            Gmaj7   Em7*
Yeah I saw sparks,
       Gmaj7   Em7*
I saw sparks,
            Gmaj7   Em7*
Yeah I saw sparks,
         Gmaj7
See me now.
```

Coda

```
         Em7*  Gmaj7
La la la, la oh,
         Em7*  Gmaj7
La la la, la oh,
         Em7*  Gmaj7
La la la, la oh,
         Em7*  Gmaj7
La la la, la oh.
```

Spies

Words & Music by Guy Berryman, Chris Martin, Jon Buckland & Will Champion

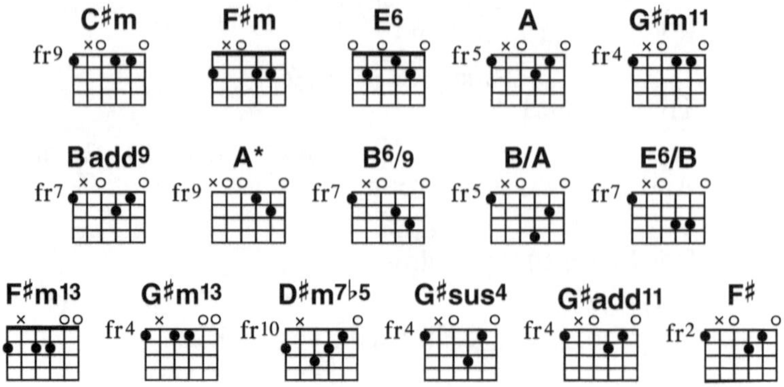

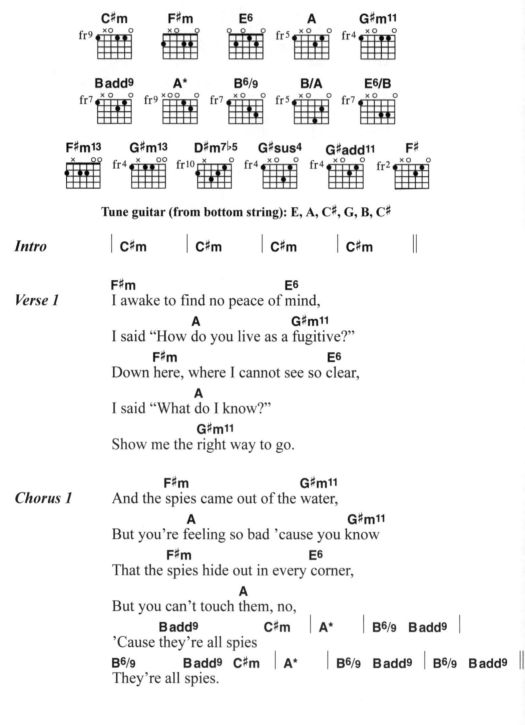

Tune guitar (from bottom string): E, A, C♯, G, B, C♯

Intro | C♯m | C♯m | C♯m | C♯m ||

Verse 1

F♯m E6
I awake to find no peace of mind,
A G♯m11
I said "How do you live as a fugitive?"
F♯m E6
Down here, where I cannot see so clear,
A
I said "What do I know?"
G♯m11
Show me the right way to go.

Chorus 1

F♯m G♯m11
And the spies came out of the water,
A G♯m11
But you're feeling so bad 'cause you know
F♯m E6
That the spies hide out in every corner,
A
But you can't touch them, no,
Badd9 C♯m | A* | B6/9 Badd9 |
'Cause they're all spies
B6/9 Badd9 C♯m | A* | B6/9 Badd9 | B6/9 Badd9 ||
They're all spies.

Verse 2

F♯m E6
I awake to see that no one is free,
A G♯m11
We're all fugitives, look at the way we live
F♯m E6
Down here, I cannot sleep from fear, no.
A
I said "Which way do I turn?"
G♯m11
Oh, I forget everything I learn.

Chorus 2

As Chorus 1

Bridge

B/A A* E6/B
And if we don't hide here
Badd9 F♯m13
They're going to find us,
G♯m13 F♯m13
If we don't hide now
Badd9 B/A
They're going to catch us where we sleep,
A* E6/B
And if we don't hide here
Badd9 | D♯m7♭5 | G♯sus4 G♯add11 ||
They're going to find us. ______

Solo

|: C♯m | A* | B6/9 Badd9 | B6/9 Badd9 :|

Chorus 3

A G♯m11
Spies came out of the water,
B/A F♯
And you're feeling so good 'cause you know
F♯m E6
That those spies hide out in every corner
A
And they can't touch you, no,
Badd9
'Cause they're just spies,
B6/9 Badd9 C♯m | A* | B6/9 Badd9 |
They're just spies.

Play 3 times

|: C♯m | A* | B6/9 Badd9 | B6/9 Badd9 :|
They're just spies.

| C♯m ||

A Spell A Rebel Yell

Words & Music by Guy Berryman, Chris Martin, Jon Buckland & Will Champion

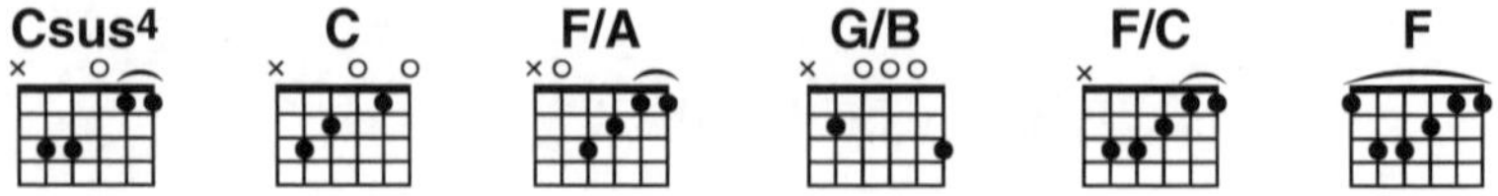

Intro

|: Csus4 C | C | Csus4 C | C :|

| F/A G/B | F/C F | Csus4 C | C |

| Csus4 C | C ||

Verse 1

Csus4 C
As far as I can see,
Csus4 C F/A G/B C/F F
All time and circuitry is wrong.

Link 1

| Csus4 C | C | Csus4 C | C ||

Verse 2

Csus4 C
As far as poetry,
Csus4 C F/A G/B F/C F
Sit down and sing to me a song.

Pre-chorus 1

Csus4 C Csus4 C
'Cause all I want in this world,
Csus4 C
All I want in this world
F/A G/B F/C F
Is for you to come home.

Chorus 1

```
Csus4   C                         Csus4   C
      A spell, a rebel yell,            a spell.
```

Verse 3

```
Csus4   C
   Sold - ier come home to me,
Csus4      C                          F/A      G/B  F/C  F
   You've been away from me so long.
```

Pre-chorus 2

```
Csus4   C        Csus4  C
         All I want   in this world,
     Csus4  C
All I want   and deserve
                      F/A      G/B  F/C  F
Is for you to come home.
```

Chorus 2

```
Csus4   C
      A spell, a rebel yell.
Csus4   C
      A spell, a rebel yell.
Csus4   C
      A spell, a rebel yell.
Csus4   C
      A spell, a rebel yell.
F/A  G/B  F/C  F
Oh.__________
Csus4   C
      A spell, a rebel yell.
Csus4   C
      A spell, a rebel yell.
Csus4   C
      A spell, a rebel yell.
Csus4   C
      A spell, a rebel yell.

F/A  G/B  F/C  F  Fade out
```

Speed Of Sound

Words & Music by Guy Berryman, Chris Martin, Jon Buckland & Will Champion

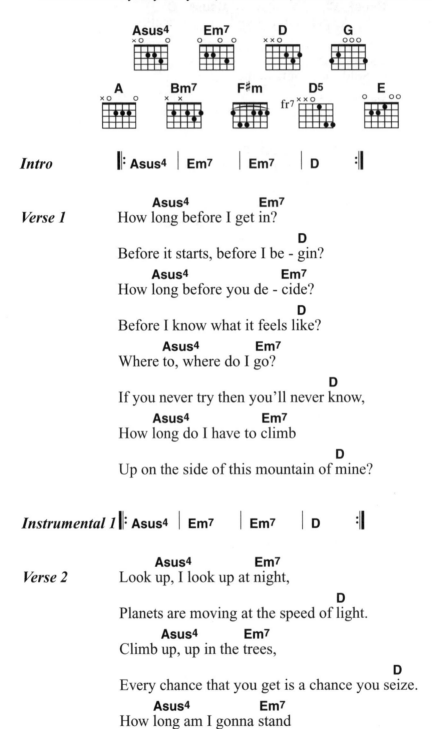

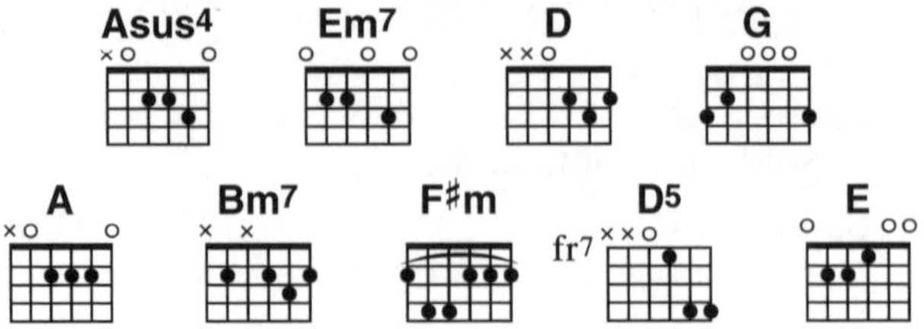

Intro ‖: Asus4 | Em7 | Em7 | D :‖

Verse 1

Asus4 Em7
How long before I get in?
D
Before it starts, before I be - gin?
Asus4 Em7
How long before you de - cide?
D
Before I know what it feels like?
Asus4 Em7
Where to, where do I go?
D
If you never try then you'll never know,
Asus4 Em7
How long do I have to climb
D
Up on the side of this mountain of mine?

Instrumental 1 ‖: Asus4 | Em7 | Em7 | D :‖

Verse 2

Asus4 Em7
Look up, I look up at night,
D
Planets are moving at the speed of light.
Asus4 Em7
Climb up, up in the trees,
D
Every chance that you get is a chance you seize.
Asus4 Em7
How long am I gonna stand

```
cont.           With my head stuck under the sand?
                     Asus4                   Em7
                I'll start before I can stop,
                                                          D
                Before I see things the right way up.

                G             A
Pre-chorus 1      All that noise
                              Bm7
                And all that sound,
                G              A                Bm7
                  All those places I got found.

                    G                             Bm7
Chorus 1        And birds go flying at the speed of sound
                   D                           G
                To show you how it all be - gan,
                                                   Bm7
                Birds came flying from the underground;
                              F#m                          G    | G    |
                If you could see it then you'd under - stand.

Instrumental 2 ||: Asus4 | Em7     | Em7     | D       :||

                    Asus4                     Em7
Verse 3         I - deas that you'll never find,
                                                           D
                All the inventors could never de - sign
                      Asus4                     Em7
                The buildings that you put up,
                                          D
                Japan and China all lit up.
                   Asus4                 Em7
                A sign that I couldn't read,
                                            D
                Or a light that I couldn't see.
                       Asus4                      Em7
                Some things you have to be - lieve,
                                                        D
                Others are puzzles, puzzling me.
```

```
                 G         A
*Pre-chorus 2*   All that noise
                                Bm7
                 And all that sound,
                 G         A              Bm7
                 All those places I got found.

                     G                              Bm7
*Chorus 2*       And birds go flying at the speed of sound
                   D                           G
                 To show you how it all be - gan,
                                                Bm7
                 Birds came flying from the underground;
                              F#m                          G
                 If you could see it then you'd under - stand,
                                F#m                          G    | G    |
                 Ah, when you see it then you'll under - stand.

Instrumental 3 | D      | D      | D      | D      |

               | D      | D      | D5     | D5     ||

                 G        A                              Bm7
*Pre-chorus 3*   All those signs, I knew what they meant,
                                E
                 Some things you can't invent,
                 G          A                      Bm7     E
                 Some get made and some get sent, ooh.___

                     G                              Bm7
*Chorus 3*       And birds go flying at the speed of sound
                   D                           G
                 To show you how it all be - gan,
                                                Bm7
                 Birds came flying from the underground,
                              F#m                          G
                 If you could see it then you'd under - stand.
                                F#m                          G
                 Ah, when you see it then you'll under - stand.

               | G      | G      | G      | G      ||
```

Square One

Words & Music by Guy Berryman, Chris Martin, Jon Buckland & Will Champion

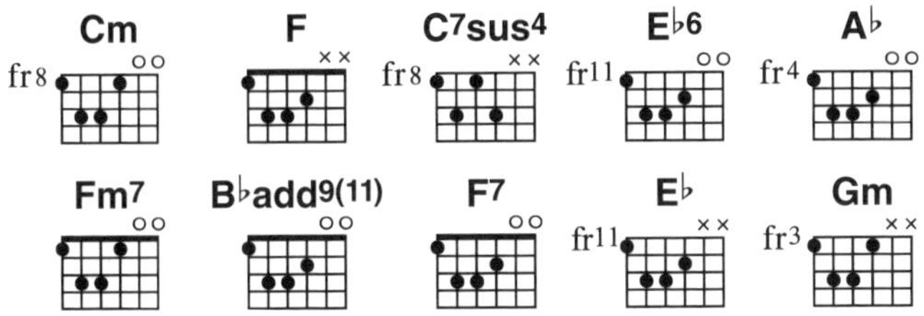

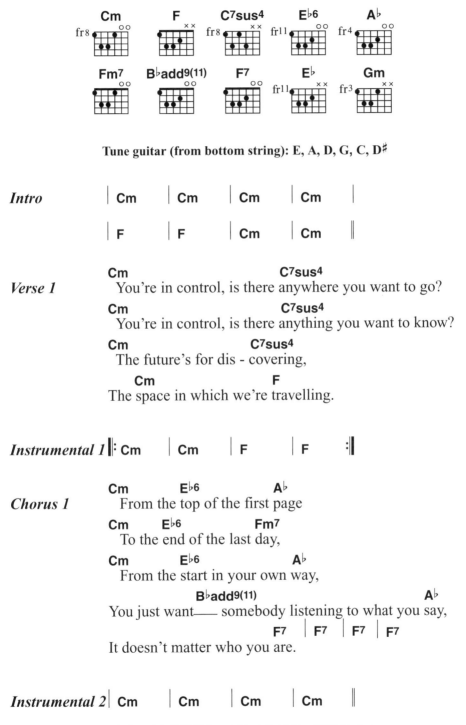

Tune guitar (from bottom string): E, A, D, G, C, D♯

Intro | Cm | Cm | Cm | Cm |
| F | F | Cm | Cm ||

Verse 1
Cm C7sus4
You're in control, is there anywhere you want to go?
Cm C7sus4
You're in control, is there anything you want to know?
Cm C7sus4
The future's for dis - covering,
Cm F
The space in which we're travelling.

Instrumental 1 ||: Cm | Cm | F | F :||

Chorus 1
Cm E♭6 A♭
From the top of the first page
Cm E♭6 Fm7
To the end of the last day,
Cm E♭6 A♭
From the start in your own way,
B♭add9(11) A♭
You just want—— somebody listening to what you say,
F7 | F7 | F7 | F7
It doesn't matter who you are.

Instrumental 2 | Cm | Cm | Cm | Cm ||

```
              E♭                          Gm            Cm
Verse 2         Under the surface trying to break through,——
              E♭                Gm            Cm
              Deciphering the codes in you.——
              E♭                  Gm                Cm
              I need a compass, draw me a map,——
                  E♭            F
              I'm on the top, I can't get back.

              | Cm       | Cm       | E♭       | F        |
              Cm
              Whoa, whoa, whoa.

              Cm          E♭6                     A♭
Chorus 2        The first line of the first page
              Cm        E♭6                  Fm7
                To the end of the last place,   you were looking...
              Cm          E♭6               A♭
                From the start in your own way,
                              B♭add9(11)                                A♭
              You just want—— somebody listening to what you say.
                                        F7
              It doesn't matter who you are,

              It doesn't matter who you are.

Instrumental 3 ||: Cm     | E♭6      | A♭       | A♭       |

              | Cm       | E♭       | Fm7      | Fm7     :||
```

Chorus 3

```
           B♭add9(11)
You just want———
                                        A♭
Somebody listening to what you say,——
                B♭add9(11)                               A♭
You just want——— somebody listening to what you say.
                              F7
It doesn't matter who you are,

It doesn't matter who you are.

|: F7    | F7    | F7    | F7    :|
```

Outro

```
         A♭
Is there anybody out there who
   Fm7
Is lost and hurt and lonely too?
         Cm                               B♭add9(11)
Are they bleeding all your colours into one?———
                          A♭
And then you come un - done

As if you've been run through,
       Fm7
Some catapult had fired you.
     Cm                             B♭add9(11)
You wonder if your chance will ever come
                             A♭
Or if you're stuck in square one.
```

Strawberry Swing

Words & Music by Guy Berryman, Chris Martin, Jon Buckland & Will Champion

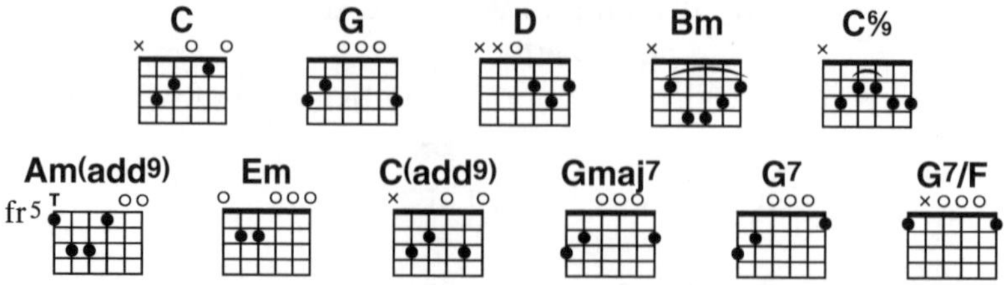

Capo first fret

Intro |: N.C. (C) | (C) | (G) | (G) |
| (D) | (D) | (D) | (D) :|

Verse 1
```
                  C
They were sit - ting,
                  G                        D
They were sit - ting on the strawberry swing.
                           C           G    D
Every moment was so precious.
```

Verse 2
```
                  C
They were sit - ting,
                   G                       D
They were talk - ing in the strawberry swing.
                        C
Everybody was for fighting,
G                            D
  Wouldn't wanna waste a thing.
               C                  G
Cold, cold water, bring me round,
               D
Now my feet won't touch the ground.
               C               G
Cold, cold water, what you say?
              Bm                         C
When it's such, it's such a perfect day,
      C6/9          G
It's such a perfect day.
```

Verse 3

```
                  C
I remem - ber
                       G                          D
We were walk - ing up to strawberry swing.
                                  C
I can't wait till the morn - ing,
G                                          D
   Wouldn't wanna change a thing.
           C                      G
People moving all the time
            D
Inside a perfectly straight line.
              C                            G
Don't you wanna just curve away?
               Bm                            C
When it's such, it's such a perfect day,
   C6/9
It's such a perfect day.
```

Interlude

```
| Am(add9) | Am(add9) | Am(add9) | Am(add9) | Em | Em |
| Em | Em | Am(add9) | Am(add9) | Am(add9) ||
Am(add9)  C(add9)
Oh I.___________
```

Bridge

```
(C(add9)) G               Gmaj7          G7
Now the sky could be blue, I don't mind,
           C                       G
With - out you it's a waste of time.
            (G)              Gmaj7          G7
(Now the sky) could be blue, I don't mind,
           C                        G
With - out you, it's a waste of time.
            (G)              Gmaj7          G7/F
(Now the sky) could be blue, could be grey,
           C                            G
With - out you I'm just miles away.
            (G)              Gmaj7            G7/F
(Now the sky) could be blue, I don't mind
           C
With - out you it's a waste of time.
```

Outro

```
| G | G | Gmaj7 | Gmaj7 |
| G7 | G7 | C | C |: G :|
                      Play 9 times
```

Such A Rush

Words & Music by Guy Berryman, Chris Martin, Jon Buckland & Will Champion

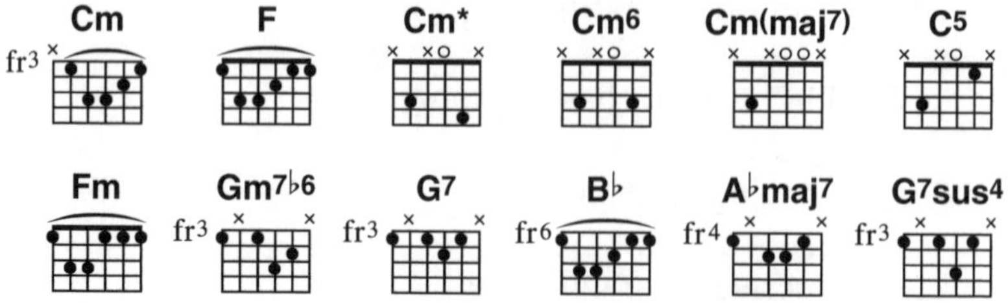

Intro

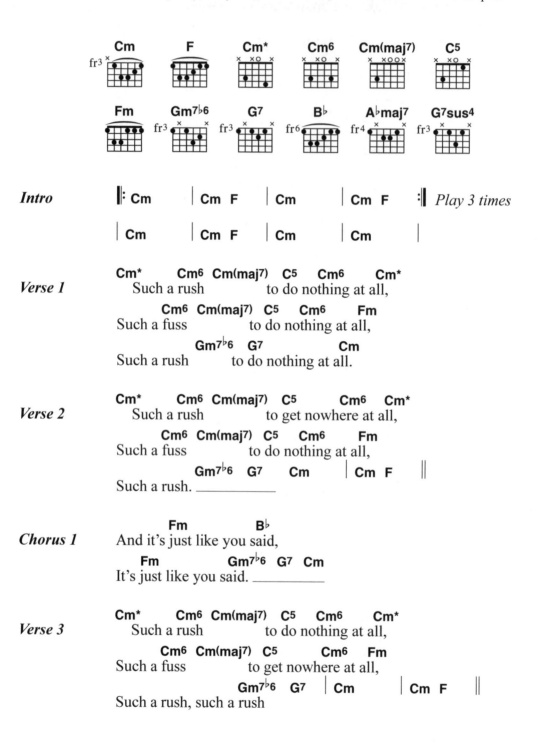

|: Cm | Cm F | Cm | Cm F :| *Play 3 times*

| Cm | Cm F | Cm | Cm |

Verse 1

Cm* Cm6 Cm(maj7) C5 Cm6 Cm*
Such a rush to do nothing at all,

Cm6 Cm(maj7) C5 Cm6 Fm
Such a fuss to do nothing at all,

Gm7♭6 G7 Cm
Such a rush to do nothing at all.

Verse 2

Cm* Cm6 Cm(maj7) C5 Cm6 Cm*
Such a rush to get nowhere at all,

Cm6 Cm(maj7) C5 Cm6 Fm
Such a fuss to do nothing at all,

Gm7♭6 G7 Cm | Cm F ||
Such a rush. ___________

Chorus 1

Fm B♭
And it's just like you said,

Fm Gm7♭6 G7 Cm
It's just like you said. ___________

Verse 3

Cm* Cm6 Cm(maj7) C5 Cm6 Cm*
Such a rush to do nothing at all,

Cm6 Cm(maj7) C5 Cm6 Fm
Such a fuss to get nowhere at all,

Gm7♭6 G7 | Cm | Cm F ||
Such a rush, such a rush

Chorus 2

```
              Fm          B♭
And it's just like you said,
   Fm            Gm7♭6  G7  A♭maj7
It's just like you said. ________
```

Bridge 1

```
            G7sus4  G7  A♭maj7
Just slow down          please
            G7sus4  G7  A♭maj7
Just slow down. ________
          G7sus4  G7  A♭maj7
So slow down          please
      G7sus4  G7  C5     | F     | C5    | F     ||
Just slow          down. ________
```

Link

```
| C5    | F     | C5    | F     ||
```

Bridge 2

```
          C5                          F
Such a rush, such a rush, such a rush, such a rush,
          C5                          F
Such a rush, such a rush, such a rush, such a rush,
          C5                          F
Such a rush, such a rush, such a rush, such a rush,
          C5                          F
Such a rush, such a rush, such a rush.
```

Verse 4

```
C5                        F
Look at all the people going after money,
C5                      F
Far too many people looking for their money.
C5                          F
Everybody's out there, trying to get money.
C5
Why can't you just tell me,
F                       C5      F
Trying to get money, rush.
```

Verse 5

```
          C5      F
Such a rush,
            C5      F
They all rush,
          C5      F
Such a rush.
          C5                          F
Such a rush, such a rush, such a rush, such a rush,
          C5                     F         C5
Such a rush, such a rush.
```

Swallowed In The Sea

Words & Music by Guy Berryman, Chris Martin, Jon Buckland & Will Champion

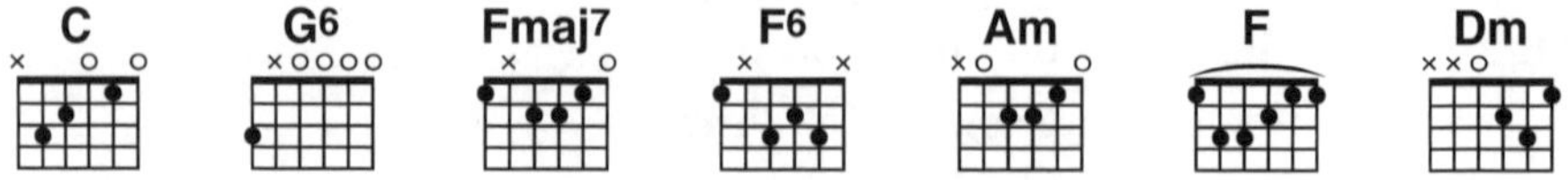

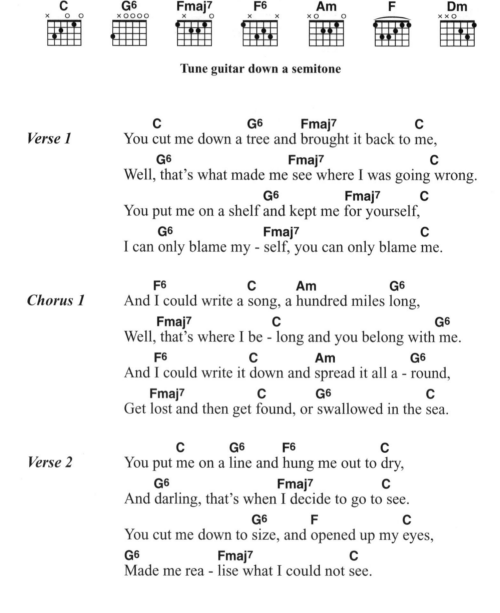

Tune guitar down a semitone

```
                C                G6        Fmaj7            C
*Verse 1*       You cut me down a tree and brought it back to me,
                   G6                     Fmaj7                   C
                Well, that's what made me see where I was going wrong.
                                 G6          Fmaj7       C
                You put me on a shelf and kept me for yourself,
                    G6              Fmaj7                 C
                I can only blame my - self, you can only blame me.

                     F6            C      Am             G6
*Chorus 1*      And I could write a song, a hundred miles long,
                   Fmaj7              C                          G6
                Well, that's where I be - long and you belong with me.
                     F6            C           Am              G6
                And I could write it down and spread it all a - round,
                    Fmaj7              C        G6               C
                Get lost and then get found, or swallowed in the sea.

                       C        G6      F6              C
*Verse 2*       You put me on a line and hung me out to dry,
                    G6                    Fmaj7         C
                And darling, that's when I decide to go to see.
                                G6        F             C
                You cut me down to size, and opened up my eyes,
                G6          Fmaj7             C
                Made me rea - lise what I could not see.
```

Chorus 2

```
       F              C          Am                 G6
And I could write a book, the one they'll say that shook
      Fmaj7            C                          G6
The world and then it took, took it back from me.
       F               C          Am               G6
And I could write it down, or spread it all a - round,
      Fmaj7            C                                G6
Get lost and then get found and you'll come back to me,
      Fmaj7            C
Not swallowed in the sea.
```

Instrumental

```
||: Dm  Fmaj7 | C    G6    | Dm  Fmaj7 | C    G6   :||
```

Chorus 3

```
       F              C        Am              G6
And I could write a song, a hundred miles long,
        Fmaj7             C                          G6
Well, that's where I be - long and you belong with me.
       F                          C    Am                G6
The streets you're walking on, a thousand houses long,
        Fmaj7             C                          G6
Well, that's where I be - long and you belong with me.
              Fmaj7         C            Am              G6
Ah, what good is it to live, with nothing left to give?
        Fmaj7              C                      G6
For - get but not for - give, not loving all you see.
       F                          C    Am                G6
The streets you're walking on, a thousand houses long,
        Fmaj7             C                          G6
Well, that's where I be - long and you belong with me,
      Fmaj7            C
Not swallowed in the sea.
Am                 G6        F6                   C
You belong with me, not swallowed in the sea,
      Am                 G6        F6                   C
Yeah, you belong with me, not swallowed in the sea.
```

Things I Don't Understand

Words & Music by Guy Berryman, Chris Martin, Jon Buckland & Will Champion

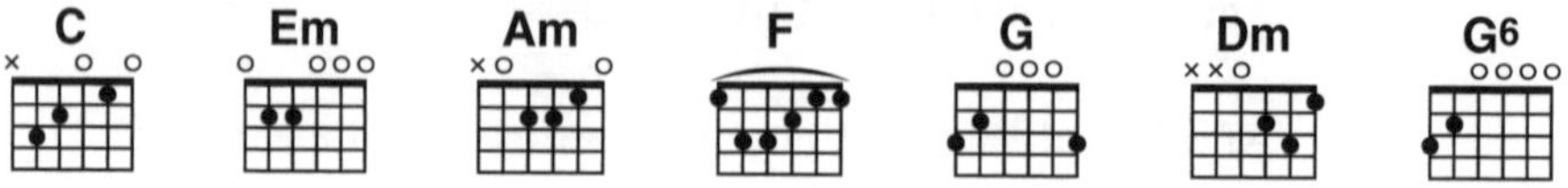

Intro

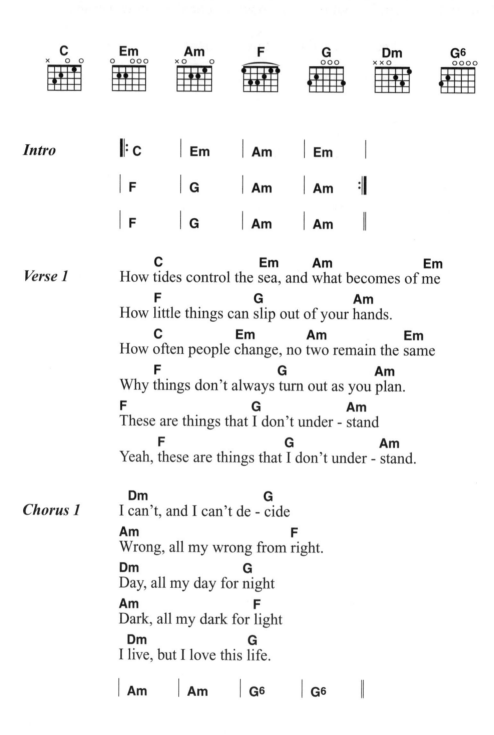

: C	Em	Am	Em
F	G	Am	Am :
F	G	Am	Am	

Verse 1

C Em Am Em
How tides control the sea, and what becomes of me
F G Am
How little things can slip out of your hands.
C Em Am Em
How often people change, no two remain the same
F G Am
Why things don't always turn out as you plan.
F G Am
These are things that I don't under - stand
F G Am
Yeah, these are things that I don't under - stand.

Chorus 1

Dm G
I can't, and I can't de - cide
Am F
Wrong, all my wrong from right.
Dm G
Day, all my day for night
Am F
Dark, all my dark for light
Dm G
I live, but I love this life.

| Am | Am | G6 | G6 ||

Link 1

```
| C    | Em   | Am   | Em   |
| F    | G    | Am   | Am   |
| F    | G    | Am   | Am   ||
```

Verse 2

```
      C         Em         Am                Em
How infinite is space, and who decides your fate
      F              G             Am
Why everything will dissolve into sand.
    C             Em          Am                Em
How to avoid de - feat, where truth and fiction meet
    F            G                  Am
Why nothing ever turns out as you planned.
F                     G               Am
These are things that I don't under - stand
      F                     G               Am
Yeah, these are things that I don't under - stand.
```

Chorus 2

```
  Dm                      G
I can't, and I can't de - cide
Am                       F
Wrong, all my wrong from right
Dm                  G
Day, all my day for night.
Am                    F
Dark, all my dark for light
  Dm                    G
I live, but I love this life.
```

```
| F    | F    | F    | F    ||
  let ring...
```

Outro

```
||: C  | Em   | Am   | Em   |
| F    | G    | Am   | Am   :||
||: F  | G    | Am   | Am   :||
| F    | G    | Am   | Am (fermata) ||
                let ring...
```

Til Kingdom Come

Words & Music by Guy Berryman, Chris Martin, Jon Buckland & Will Champion

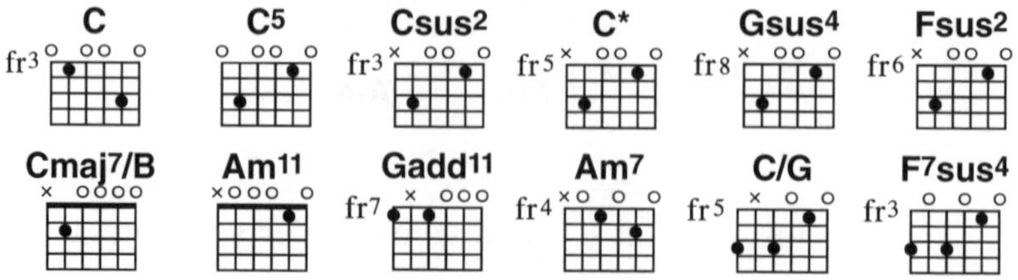

Tune guitar (from bottom string): C, A, C, G, B, C

Intro | C | C | C | C ||

Verse 1

C5 Csus2 C* Csus2 C
Still my— heart and hold my— tongue,
C5 Csus2 C* Csus2 C
I feel my— time, my time has come.
C5 Csus2 C* Csus2 C
Let me— in, un - lock the door,
Gsus4 C* Fsus2 Csus2 C* Cmaj7/B C
I nev - er— felt— this— way— be - fore.

Pre-chorus 1

Am11 Fsus2 C
The wheels just keep on turn - ing,
Am11 Fsus2 C
The drummer be - gins to drum,
Am11 Fsus2 C
I don't know which way I'm go - ing,
Fsus2 Gsus4 C Csus2
I don't know which way I've come.

Instrumental 1 | C* | C* Csus2 | C5 ||

Verse 2

C5 Csus2 C* Csus2 C
Hold— my— head in - side your hands,
C5 Csus2 C* Csus2 C
I need some - one who under - stands,

cont.

C5 Csus2 C* Csus2 C
I need some - one; some - one who hears,
Gsus4 C* Fsus2 Csus2 C* Cmaj7/B C
For you— I've wait - ed— all these— years.

Chorus 1

Fsus2 C
For you I'd wait til kingdom come,
Fsus2 C
Until my day, my day is done.
Fsus2 Gadd11 Am7
Say you'll come and set me— free,
C/G F7sus4 C Csus2
Just say you'll wait,— you'll wait for me.

Instrumental 2 | C* | C* Csus2 | C5 ||

Verse 3

C5 Csus2 C* Csus2 C
In— your— tears and in your blood,
C5 Csus2 C* Csus2 C
In— your— fire and in your flood,
C5 Csus2 C* Csus2 C
I heard you— laugh, I heard you sing,
Gsus4 C* Fsus2 Csus2 C* Cmaj7/B C
I would - n't— change a— sin - gle— thing.

Pre-chorus 2

Am11 Fsus2 C
The wheels just keep on turn - ing,
Am11 Fsus2 C
The drummers be - gin to drum.
Am11 Fsus2 C
I don't know which way I'm go - ing,
Fsus2 Gsus4 C
I don't know which way I've come.

Chorus 2

Fsus2 C
For you I'd wait til kingdom come,
Fsus2 C
Until my days, my days are done.
Fsus2 Gadd11 Am7
Say you'll come and set me— free,
C/G F7sus4 C
Just say you'll wait,— you'll wait for me.
C/G F7sus4 C
Just say you'll wait,— you'll wait for me.
C/G F7sus4 C
Just say you'll wait,— you'll wait for me.

Trouble

Words & Music by Guy Berryman, Chris Martin, Jon Buckland & Will Champion

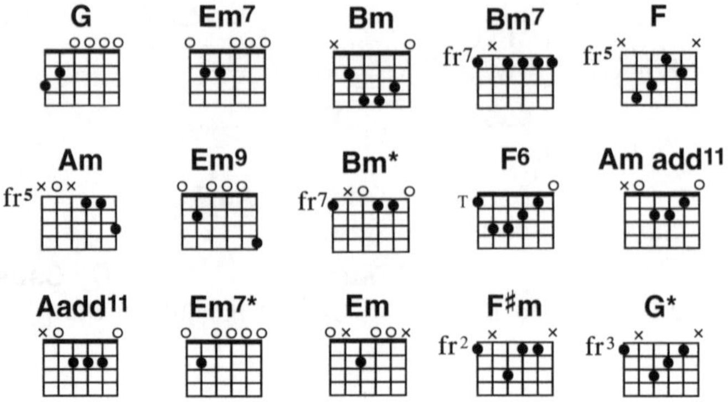

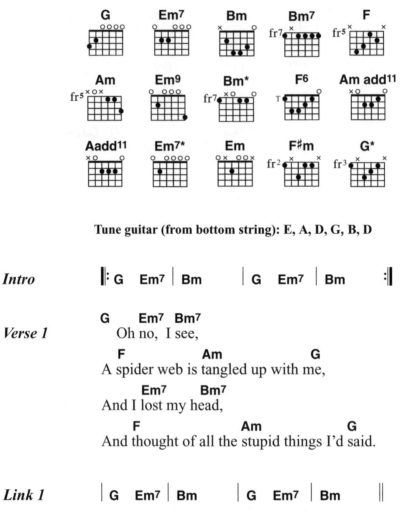

Tune guitar (from bottom string): E, A, D, G, B, D

Intro ‖: G Em7 | Bm | G Em7 | Bm :‖

Verse 1

```
G       Em7  Bm7
   Oh no, I see,
  F              Am             G
A spider web is tangled up with me,
       Em7        Bm7
And I lost my head,
     F                   Am          G
And thought of all the stupid things I'd said.
```

Link 1 | G Em7 | Bm | G Em7 | Bm ‖

Verse 2

```
G       Em9       Bm*
   Oh no, what's this?
  F6                    Am add11
A spider web, and I'm caught in the middle,
G        Em9     Bm*
   So I turn to run,
     F6                  Am add11    G
And thought of all the stupid things I'd done.
```

Chorus 1

Aadd11 Em7
And ah, I never meant to cause you trouble,
Aadd11 Em7
And ah, I never meant to do you wrong,
Aadd11 Em7
And ah, well if I ever caused you trouble,
Aadd11 Em7
Then oh, I never meant to do you harm.

Link 2

| G Em7 | Bm | G Em7 | Bm ||

Verse 3

G Em9 Bm*
Oh no, I see,
F6 Amadd11
A spider web and it's me in the middle,
G Em7 Bm*
So I twist and turn,
F6 Amadd11 G
But here I am in my little bubble.

Chorus 2

Aadd11 Em7
Singing out ah, I never meant to cause you trouble,
Aadd11 Em7
And ah, I never meant to do you wrong,
Aadd11 Em7
And ah, well if I ever caused you trouble,
Aadd11 Em7
Then oh no I never meant to do you harm.

Link 3

||: G Em9 | Bm* | G Em9 | Bm* :||

Coda

Em F♯m G* F♯m Em
And they spun a web for me,
F♯m G* F♯m Em
And they spun a web for me,
F♯m G* F♯m Em | Em |
And they spun a web for me.

||: G Em7 | Bm* | G Em7 | Bm* :||

Twisted Logic

Words & Music by Guy Berryman, Chris Martin, Jon Buckland & Will Champion

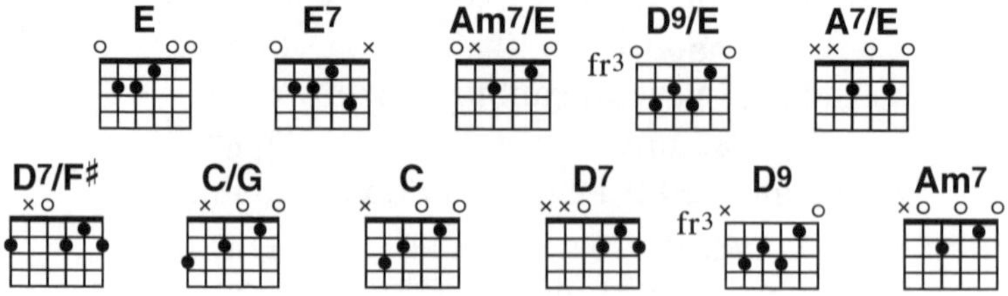

Tune guitar down a semitone

Verse 1

E E7 Am7/E
Sunlight— opened up my eyes,
D9/E E E7
To see for the first time
Am7/E D9/E
It opened them up,
E E7 Am7/E D9/E
And tonight,— rivers will run dry,
E E7 A7/E D9/E
And not for the first time,— rivers will run.

Instrumental 1 ‖: D7/F♯ | C/G | C | D7 :‖

Verse 2

E E7 Am7/E D9/E
Hundreds— of years in the future
E E7
There could be com - puters
Am7/E D9/E E
Looking for life— on— Earth,
E7 Am7/E D9/E
So don't fight for the wrong side,
E E7
Say what you feel like,
A7/E D9/E
Say how you feel.———

Instrumental 2 | C | D9 | E | Am7 |

| C | D9 | E | Am7 ‖

```
               C                D9
Chorus 1       You'll go backwards a - gain,
               E                Am7
               You'll go forwards a - gain,
               C                D9
               You'll go backwards a - gain, you'll go.


Instrumental 3 ||: E      | E7      | Am7/E   | D9/E    :||


                  E  E7                        Am7/E      D9/E
Verse 3        Creat - ed— then drilled and in - vaded,
                           E        E7
               If somebody made it,
                            Am7/E   D9/E   E
               Someone will mess— it—   up.
               E7                 Am7/E    D9/E
               And you are not wrong to
                                        E       E7
               Ask, "Who does this be - long to?"
                              Am7/E   D9/E
               It belongs to all— of us.


Instrumental 4 ||: D7/F#  | C/G     | C       | D7      :|| E       | E       ||


               C                D9
Chorus 2       You'll go backwards a - gain,
               E                Am7
               You'll go forwards a - gain,
               C                D9
               You'll go backwards a - gain,
               E
               You'll go forwards.
               C                D9
               You'll go backwards a - gain,
               E                Am7
               You'll go forwards a - gain,
               C                D9
               You'll go backwards a - gain,
               E
               You'll go forwards.


Instrumental 5 | C       | D9      | E       | Am7     |
                                     𝄐
               | C       | D9      | E       ||
```

Violet Hill

Words & Music by Guy Berryman, Chris Martin, Jon Buckland & Will Champion

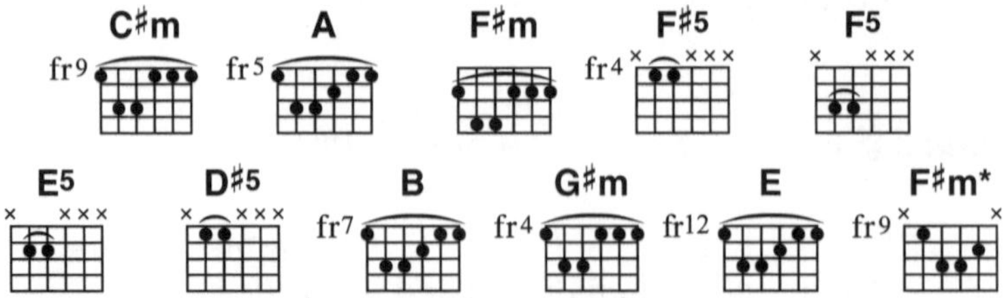

Verse 1

```
          C♯m
Was a long and dark December,

From the rooftops I remember
              A              F♯m    F♯5  F5  E5  D♯5
There was snow, white snow.
C♯m
Clearly I remember

From the windows they were watching
             A                 F♯m    F♯5  F5  E5  D♯5
While we froze down be - low.
             A
When the future's architectured
    B                    C♯m
By a carnival of idiots on show,
                 B
You'd better lie low.
G♯m    A    G♯m  E           C♯m   B     C♯m
If you love me     won't you let    me know?
```

Verse 2

```
C♯m
Was a long and dark December

When the banks became cathedrals
            A             F♯m    F♯5  F5  E5  D♯5
And the fox became God.
```

```
              C#m
cont.         Priests clutched onto bibles

              Hollowed out to fit their rifles
                   A                   F#m   F#5  F5  E5  D#5
              And the cross was held a - loft.
              A
              Bury me in armour,
                     B
              When I'm dead and hit the ground,
                C#m                      B
              My nerves are poles that un - fold.
                 G#m  A   G#m  E        C#m  B    C#m
              And if you love me   won't you let  me know?


Instr.        |: C#m   | C#m   | A     | F#m  F#5  F5  E5  D#5 :|

                    A
Verse 3       I don't want to be a soldier
                  B
              Who the captain of some sinking ship
                  C#m      B
              Would stow far be - low.
                G#m  A   G#m  E        C#m  B    C#m
              So if you love me   why'd you let  me go?

              A  C#m    F#m*      E   C#m   B  A
Outro            I took my love down to vio - let hill,
                     B  C#m  G#m  A
              There we sat     in   snow.
                    B  C#m F#m*  E  C#m   B
              All that time    she was si - lent still.
                G#m  A   G#m  E        C#m  B     A
              So if you love me   won't you let  me know?
              G#m  A  G#m  E        C#m  B    C#m
              If you love me,  won't you let  me know?
```

Viva La Vida

Words & Music by Guy Berryman, Chris Martin, Jon Buckland & Will Champion

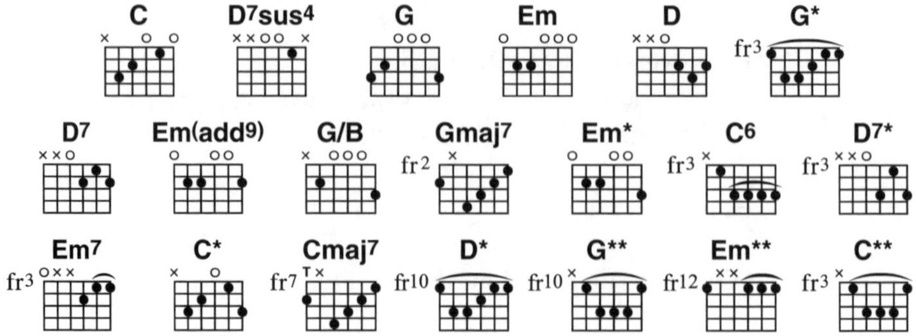

Capo first fret

Intro

| C | D7sus4 | G | Em |
| C | D7sus4 | G | Em ||

Verse 1

```
(Em)        C          D7sus4
I used to rule the world,
                 G                        Em
Seas would rise when I gave the word.
                                   C          D7sus4
Now in the morning I sleep a - lone,
                G                  Em
Sweep the streets I used to own.
```

Interlude 1

| C | D | G* | Em |
| C | D | G* | Em ||

Verse 2

(Em) C D7sus4
I used to roll the dice,
G Em
Feel the fear in my enemy's eyes.
C D7sus4
Listened as the crowd would sing:
G Em
"Now the old king is dead, long live the king."
C D7sus4
One minute I held the key,
G Em
Next the walls were closed on me.
C D7sus4
And I discovered that my castles stand
G Em
Upon pillars of salt and pil - lars of sand.

Chorus 1

C D7
I hear Jerusalem bells a-ringing,
G Em(add9)
Roman cavalry choirs are singing.
C D7
Be my mirror my sword and shield,
G Em(add9)
My missionaries in a foreign field.
C D7
For some reason I can't explain,
G/B Em(add9)
Once you'd gone there was never,
C D7
Never an ho - nest word,
Gmaj7 Em*
And that was when I ruled the world.

Interlude 2

C6	D7*	G*	Em7
C6	D7*	G*	Em7 ‖

Verse 3

```
(Em7)                     C     D7sus4
It was the wicked and wild wind,
                  G              Em
Blew down the doors to let me in.
                              C          D7sus4
Shattered windows and the sound of drums,
         G                      Em
People couldn't believe what I'd become.
              C      D7sus4
Revolution - aries wait
         G                Em
For my head on a silver plate.
                       C       D7sus4
Just a puppet on a lonely string,
     G                          Em
Oh, who would ever want to be king?
```

Chorus 2

```
  C                 D7
I hear Jerusalem bells a-ringing,
G                Em(add9)
Roman cavalry choirs are singing.
C                  D7
Be my mirror my sword and shield,
     G                   Em(add9)
My missionaries in a foreign field.
C                    D7
For some reason I can't explain,
  G/B                      Em(add9)
I know St. Peter won't call my name.
        C        D7
Never an honest word,
                Gmaj7          Em
But that was when I ruled the world.
```

Interlude 3 | C* | Em* | C* | Em* |

| C* | Em* | D7* ||

```
(D7*)                  C   D
Oh, oh, oh, oh, oh,    oh.
                       G   Em(add9)
Oh, oh, oh, oh, oh,    oh.
                       C   D7
Oh, oh, oh, oh, oh,    oh.
                       G   Em(add9)
Oh, oh, oh, oh, oh,    oh.

Oh, oh, oh, oh, oh.
```

Chorus 3

```
C                D7
Hear Jerusalem bells a-ringing,
G                Em(add9)
Roman cavalry choirs are singing.
C                  D7
Be my mirror my sword and shield,
   G                     Em(add9)
My missionaries in a foreign field.
C                   D7
For some reason I can't explain,
 G/B                      Em(add9)
I know St. Peter won't call my name.
          Cmaj7  D*
Never an honest word,
              G**                Em**
But that was when I ruled the world.
```

Outro | C** | D | Gmaj7 | Em7 |

| C** | D | Gmaj7 | Em7 || *Repeat to fade*

Talk

Words & Music by Guy Berryman, Chris Martin, Karl Bartos,
Jon Buckland, Will Champion, Emil Schult & Ralf Hütter

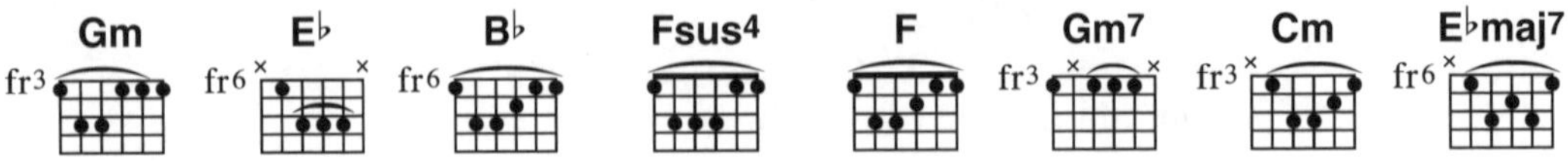

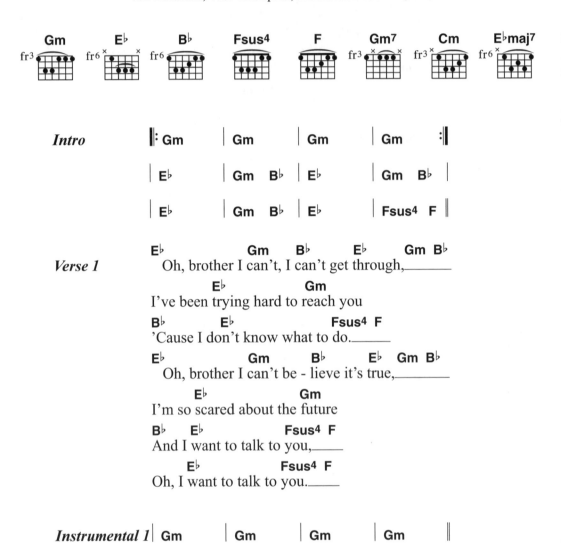

Intro | ‖: Gm | Gm | Gm | Gm :‖ |
| E♭ | Gm B♭ | E♭ | Gm B♭ |
| E♭ | Gm B♭ | E♭ | Fsus4 F ‖

Verse 1

```
E♭               Gm      B♭        E♭          Gm  B♭
   Oh, brother I can't, I can't get through,______
           E♭               Gm
I've been trying hard to reach you
B♭          E♭                  Fsus4  F
'Cause I don't know what to do.______
E♭               Gm          B♭         E♭   Gm  B♭
   Oh, brother I can't be - lieve it's true,________
        E♭                  Gm
I'm so scared about the future
B♭      E♭               Fsus4  F
And I want to talk to you,_____
       E♭                Fsus4  F
Oh, I want to talk to you._____
```

Instrumental 1 | Gm | Gm | Gm | Gm ‖

Chorus 1

E♭ Gm7 B♭ E♭ Gm7 B♭
You could take a picture of something you see,
E♭ Gm7 B♭ E♭ Gm7 B♭
In the future where will I be?
E♭ Gm7 B♭ E♭ Gm7 B♭
You could climb a ladder up to the sun,
E♭ Gm7 B♭
Or write a song no - body had sung
E♭ Fsus4 F
Or do something that's never been done.

Instrumental 2 | Gm7 | Gm7 | Gm7 | Gm7 ||

Verse 2

E♭ Gm B♭ E♭ Gm B♭
Are you lost or incom - plete?
E♭ Gm B♭
Do you feel like a puzzle;
E♭ Fsus4 F
You can't find your missing piece?___
E♭ Gm B♭ E♭ Gm B♭
Tell me how you feel,___
E♭ Gm B♭ E♭ Fsus4 F
Well, I feel like they're talking in a language I don't speak,___
E♭ Fsus4 F
And they're talking it to me.___

Instrumental 3 | Gm | Gm | Gm | Gm ||

Chorus 2

E♭ Gm7 B♭ E♭ Gm7 B♭
So you could take a picture of something you see,
E♭ Gm7 B♭ E♭ Gm7 B♭
In the future where will I be?
E♭ Gm7 B♭ E♭ Gm7 B♭
You could climb a ladder up to the sun,
E♭ Gm7 B♭
Or write a song no - body had sung
Fsus4 F
Or do something that's never been done,
E♭ Fsus4 F
Do something that's never been done.

Instrumental 4 | Gm7 | Gm7 | Gm7 | Gm7 |

||: Cm | E♭ | Gm | F |

| Cm | E♭ | Gm | F :||

Guitar solo | E♭ | Gm B♭ | E♭ | Gm B♭ |

| E♭ | Gm B♭ | E♭ | Fsus4 F ||

Chorus 3

```
             E♭
So you don't know where you're going
                  Gm7     B♭  E♭  Gm7  B♭
And you want to talk,
       E♭
You feel like you're going
                          Gm7       B♭  E♭  Gm7  B♭
Where you've been be - fore,
                 E♭
You'll tell anyone who'll listen
                 Gm7     B♭  E♭  Gm7  B♭
But you feel ig - nored,
       E♭                                   Gm7     B♭
And nothing's really making any sense at all.
        E♭          F
Let's talk, let's talk,
        E♭maj7     F     Gm
Let's talk, let's talk.
```

Warning Sign

Words & Music by Guy Berryman, Chris Martin, Jon Buckland & Will Champion

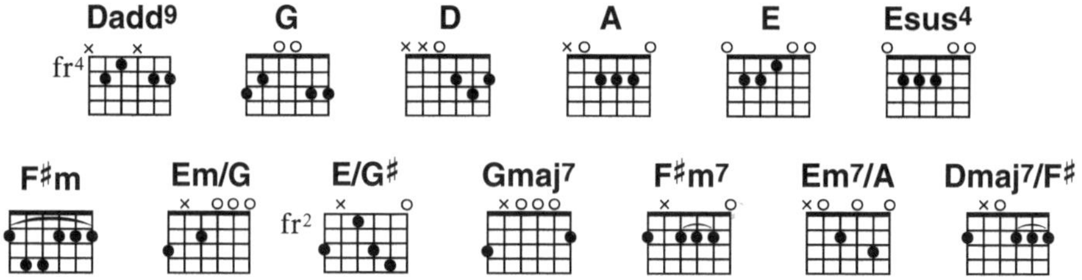

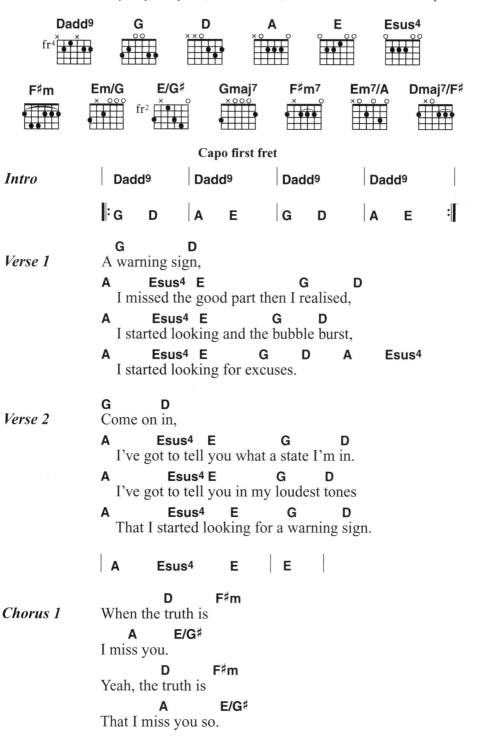

Capo first fret

Intro | Dadd9 | Dadd9 | Dadd9 | Dadd9 |

|: G D | A E | G D | A E :|

Verse 1

G D
A warning sign,
A Esus4 E G D
I missed the good part then I realised,
A Esus4 E G D
I started looking and the bubble burst,
A Esus4 E G D A Esus4
I started looking for excuses.

Verse 2

G D
Come on in,
A Esus4 E G D
I've got to tell you what a state I'm in.
A Esus4 E G D
I've got to tell you in my loudest tones
A Esus4 E G D
That I started looking for a warning sign.

| A Esus4 E | E |

Chorus 1

D F♯m
When the truth is
A E/G♯
I miss you.
D F♯m
Yeah, the truth is
A E/G♯
That I miss you so.

Guitar solo | G D | A Esus4 E | G D | A Esus4 E |

Verse 3

```
 G         D
A warning sign
A       Esus4        E
   You came back to haunt me
     G         D
And I realised,
A                Esus4  E
   That you were an island
     G            D
And I passed you by,
A                Esus4  E           G        D
   When you were an island to discover.
```

| A Esus4 E |

Verse 4

```
G          D
Come on in,
A          Esus4   E           G         D
   I've got to tell you what a state I'm in.
A          Esus4   E           G        D
   I've got to tell you in my loudest tones
A          Esus4      E        G         D
   That I started looking for a warning sign.
```

| A Esus4 E | E |

Chorus 2

```
              D        F#m
When the truth is
      A       E/G#
I miss you.
              D        F#m
Yeah, the truth is
             A          E/G#
That I miss you so.
             Gmaj7  F#m7
And I'm tired,
                         A        E/G# | E/G# |
I should not have let you go.
```

Middle

| A | Em7/A | G | Dmaj7/F♯ |
Oh.

| A | Em7/A | G | Dmaj7/F♯ |

Outro

```
         A     Em7/A          G            Dmaj7/F♯
So I crawl back into your open arms.
          A     Em7/A          G           Dmaj7/F♯
Yes I crawl back into your open arms.
           A     Em7/A          G          Dmaj7/F♯
And I crawl back into your open arms.
          A     Em7/A                      F♯m (pause)
Yes I crawl back into your open arms.
```

We Never Change

Words & Music by Guy Berryman, Chris Martin, Jon Buckland & Will Champion

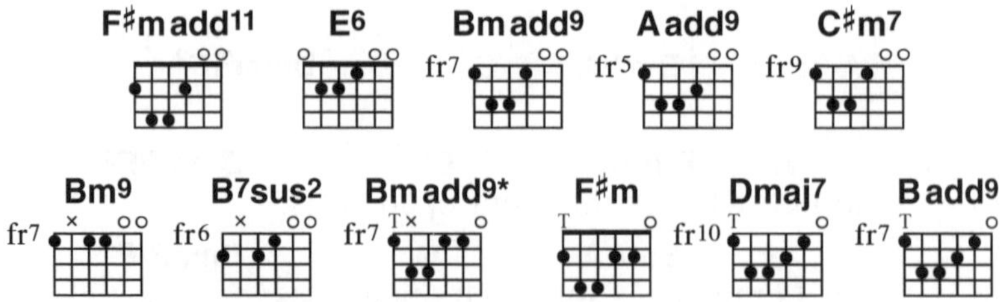

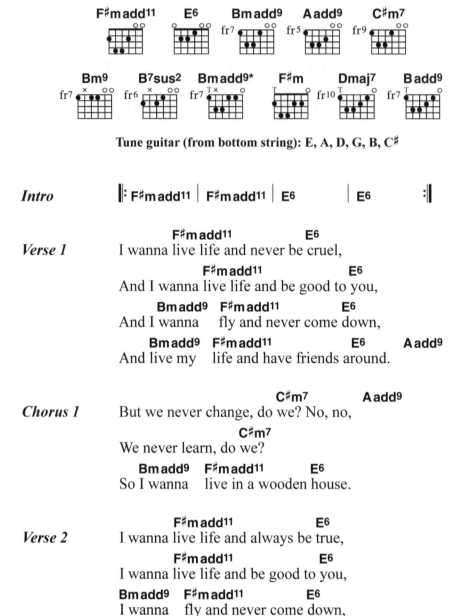

Tune guitar (from bottom string): E, A, D, G, B, C♯

Intro ‖: F♯madd11 | F♯madd11 | E6 | E6 :‖

Verse 1

F♯madd11 E6
I wanna live life and never be cruel,
F♯madd11 E6
And I wanna live life and be good to you,
Bmadd9 F♯madd11 E6
And I wanna fly and never come down,
Bmadd9 F♯madd11 E6 Aadd9
And live my life and have friends around.

Chorus 1

C♯m7 Aadd9
But we never change, do we? No, no,
C♯m7
We never learn, do we?
Bmadd9 F♯madd11 E6
So I wanna live in a wooden house.

Verse 2

F♯madd11 E6
I wanna live life and always be true,
F♯madd11 E6
I wanna live life and be good to you,
Bmadd9 F♯madd11 E6
I wanna fly and never come down,
Bmadd9 F♯madd11 E6 Aadd9
And live my life and have friends around.

Chorus 2

C♯m7 Aadd9
But we never change, do we? No, no,

C♯m7
We never learn, do we?

Bmadd9 F♯madd11 E6
So I wanna live in a wooden house,

Bmadd9 F♯madd11 E6
Where making more friends would be easy.

Bridge

Bm9 B7sus2 Bm9 B7sus2 E6 Bm9
Oh, I don't have a soul to save,

B7sus2 Bm9 B7sus2 E6 Bmadd9
Yes, and I sin every single day.

Chorus 3

F♯madd11 E6 Bmadd9
We never change, do we?

F♯madd11 E6
We never learn, do we?

Outro

Bmadd9 F♯m E6 Bmadd9*
So I wanna live in a wooden house,

F♯m Dmaj7 Badd9
Where making more friends would be ea - sy.

Bmadd9 F♯m E6 Bmadd9
I wanna live where the sun comes out.

What If

Words & Music by Guy Berryman, Chris Martin, Jon Buckland & Will Champion

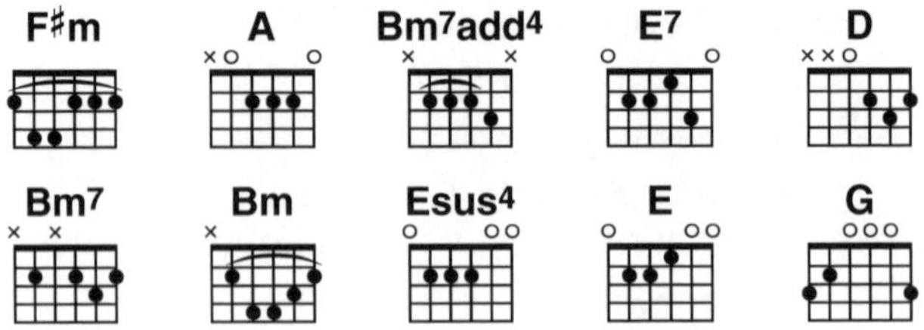

Verse 1

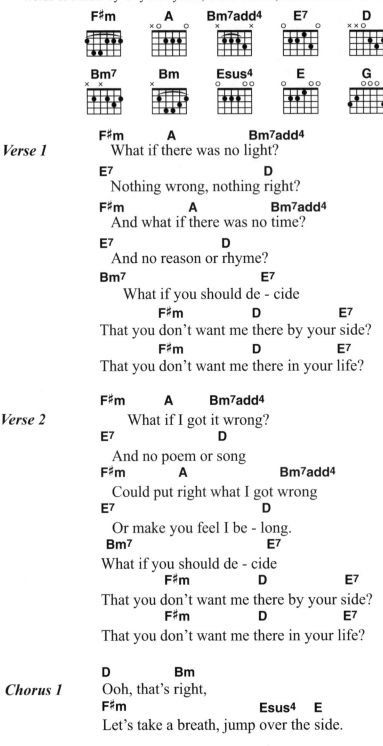

F♯m A Bm7add4
What if there was no light?
E7 D
Nothing wrong, nothing right?
F♯m A Bm7add4
And what if there was no time?
E7 D
And no reason or rhyme?
Bm7 E7
What if you should de - cide
F♯m D E7
That you don't want me there by your side?
F♯m D E7
That you don't want me there in your life?

Verse 2

F♯m A Bm7add4
What if I got it wrong?
E7 D
And no poem or song
F♯m A Bm7add4
Could put right what I got wrong
E7 D
Or make you feel I be - long.
Bm7 E7
What if you should de - cide
F♯m D E7
That you don't want me there by your side?
F♯m D E7
That you don't want me there in your life?

Chorus 1

D Bm
Ooh, that's right,
F♯m Esus4 E
Let's take a breath, jump over the side.

```
            D           Bm
cont.       Ooh, that's right,
            F#m                              Esus4      E
            How can you know it when you don't even try?
            D           Bm
            Ooh, that's right.

            F#m    A               Bm7add4
Verse 3       Every step that you take
            E7                             D
              Could be your biggest mis - take,
            F#m      A                 Bm7add4
              It could bend or it could break
            E7                            D
              But that's the risk that you take.
            Bm7                         E7
                What if you should de - cide
                      F#m            D              E7
            That you don't want me there in your life?
                      F#m            D              E7
            That you don't want me there by your side?

            D           Bm
Chorus 2    Ooh, that's right,
            F#m                      Esus4    E
            Let's take a breath, jump over the side,
            D           Bm
            Ooh, that's right.
            F#m                              Esus4      E
            How can you know it when you don't even try?
            G           D        E
            Ooh, that's right.

            D           Bm
            Ooh, that's right,
Chorus 3    F#m                      Esus4    E
            Let's take a breath, jump over the side,
            D           Bm
            Ooh, that's right.
            F#m                              Esus4      E
            You know that darkness always turns into light,
            G           D        E
            Ooh, that's right.
```

A Whisper

Words & Music by Guy Berryman, Chris Martin, Jon Buckland & Will Champion

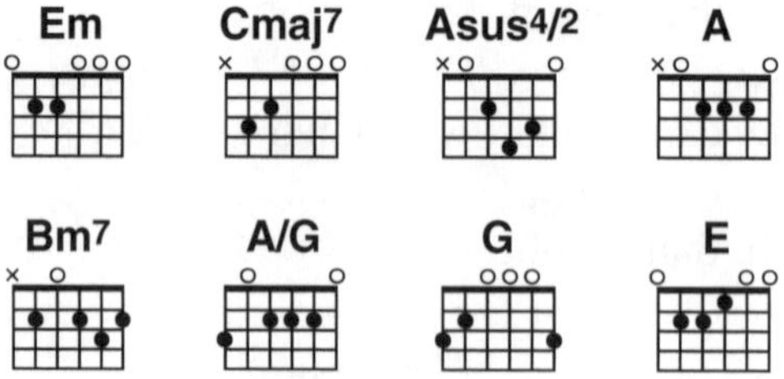

Capo third fret

Intro | ‖: Em | Em | Em | Em :‖

Chorus 1

Cmaj7 Em
A whisper, a whisper, a whisper, a whisper.
Cmaj7 (Em)
A whisper, a whisper, a whisper, a whisper.

Link 1 | Em | Em | Em | Em ‖

Verse 1

Asus4/2 A Asus4/2 A
I hear the sound of the ticking of clocks,
Asus4/2 A
Who remembers your face,
Asus4/2 A Em
Who remembers you when you are (gone?)

Link 2 | Em | Em | Em | Em ‖
gone?

Verse 2

Asus4/2 A Asus4/2 A
I hear the sound of the ticking of clocks
Asus4/2 A
Come back and look for me,
Asus4/2 A Em
Look for me when I am lost.

Chorus 2

Cmaj7 Em
And just a whisper, a whisper, a whisper, a whisper.
Cmaj7 (Em)
Just a whisper, a whisper, a whisper, a whisper.

Link 3 | Em | Em | Em | Em ||

Middle

```
Bm7            Cmaj7     A
Night turns to day, and I still have these questions,
Bm7          Cmaj7              A
Bridges will break, should I go forwards or backwards?
    Bm7            Cmaj7     A                       A/G
And night turns to day, and I still get no answers.

| Em | Em |
```

Chorus 3

```
Cmaj7                                           Em
  A whisper, a whisper, a whisper, a whisper.
   Cmaj7                                          Em
Just a whisper, a whisper, a whisper, a whisper.
```

Link 4 | Em | Em | Em |

Verse 3

```
Asus4/2  A              Asus4/2  A
I hear the sound of the ticking of clocks,
    Asus4/2          A
Who remembers your face,
      Asus4/2       A           Em     | Em |
Who remembers you when you are gone?
```

Verse 4

```
Asus4/2  A              Asus4/2  A
I hear the sound of the ticking of clocks
Asus4/2           A
Come back and look for me,
Asus4/2     A        Em
Look for me when I am lost.
```

Chorus 4

```
       Cmaj7                                          Em
And just a whisper, a whisper, a whisper, a whisper.
   Cmaj7
Just a whisper, a whisper, a whisper, a whisper.
```

Link 4 | E | E | E | E ||

Outro

```
||: G   A | E     | G   A | E     |
|   G   A | E     | G   A | E     :||  Repeat to fade
```

White Shadows

Words & Music by Guy Berryman, Chris Martin, Jon Buckland & Will Champion

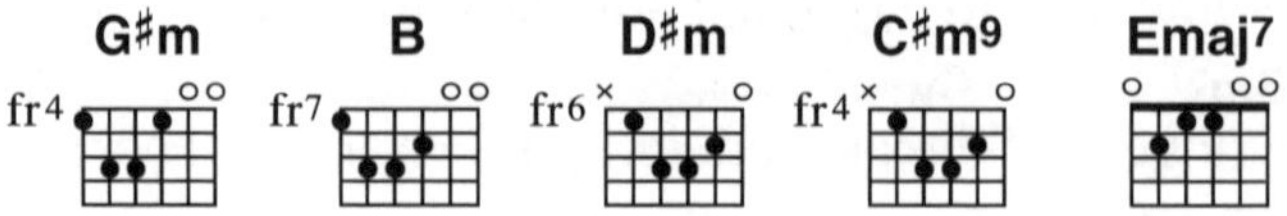

Tune top string to D♯

```
Intro          | G♯m   | G♯m   ||: G♯m   | B     | D♯m   | C♯m9  :||

               G♯m              B
Verse 1          When I was a young boy
                 D♯m    C♯m9
               I tried to listen
               G♯m              B          D♯m
                 And I want to feel like that...
               G♯m            B           D♯m        C♯m9
                 Little white shadows, blink and miss them,
               G♯m          B          D♯m
                 Part of a system I am.

Instrumental 1 | G♯m   | G♯m   | D♯m   | C♯m9  |

               | G♯m   | G♯m   | D♯m   | D♯m   ||

               G♯m           B         D♯m          C♯m9
Verse 2          If you ever feel like something's missing,
               G♯m                  B        D♯m
                 Things you never under - stand,
               G♯m           B          D♯m                C♯m9
                 Little white shadows sparkle and glis - ten,
               G♯m          B          D♯m
                 Part of a system, a plan.
```

Pre-chorus1

```
Emaj7                C#m9
  All this noise I'm waking up,
Emaj7                C#m9
  All the space I'm taking up,
Emaj7               C#m9
  All this sound is breaking up,
Emaj7           C#m9
  Whoa, whoa.___
```

Chorus1

```
G#m                        Emaj7
Maybe you'll get what you wanted,
B                          D#m
Maybe you'll stumble up - on it.
G#m                  Emaj7      B            D#m
Everything you ever wanted, in a permanent state,
G#m                              Emaj7
Maybe you'll know when you've seen it,
B                         D#m
Maybe if you say it you'll mean it,
G#m                         Emaj7
And when you find it you'll keep it
    B                D#m                    (G#m)
In a permanent state,   a permanent state.
```

Instrumental 2

```
| G#m     | G#m     | D#m     | C#m9    |
(state.)
| G#m     | G#m     | D#m     | C#m9    ||
```

Verse3

```
G#m             B
  When I was a young boy
 D#m          C#m9
  I tried to lis - ten,
G#m                 B       D#m
  Don't you want to feel like that?
G#m                 B
  You're part of the human race,
D#m                          C#m9
  All of the stars and the outer space...
G#m        B          D#m
  Part of a system I am.
```

```
                    Emaj7                   C#m9
*Pre-chorus 2*        All this noise I'm waking up,
                    Emaj7                  C#m9
                      All the space I'm taking up,
                    Emaj7                      C#m9
                      I cannot hear, you're breaking up,
                    Emaj7             C#m9
                      Whoa, whoa.___

                    G#m                          Emaj7
Chorus 2            Maybe you'll get what you wanted,
                    B                            D#m
                    Maybe you'll stumble up - on it,
                    G#m                     Emaj7        B              D#m
                    Everything you ever wanted, in a permanent state.
                    G#m                                 Emaj7
                    Maybe you'll know when you've seen it,
                    B                           D#m
                    Maybe if you say it you'll mean it,
                    G#m                            Emaj7
                    And when you find it you'll keep it
                          B              D#m              (G#m)
                    In a permanent state,    a permanent state.

Instrumental 3      ||: G#m    | G#m    | Emaj7  | Emaj7  |
                    (state.)
                    | B        | B      | D#m    | D#m   :||

                    G#m
Outro                 Swim out on a sea of faces,
                    Emaj7
                      The tide of the human races,
                    B
                    Oh, an answer now is what I need.
                    G#m
                      See it in the new sun rise and
                    Emaj7
                      See it breaking on your horizon.
                    B
                    Oh, come on love;
                              D#m   G#m
                    Stay with me.___
```

The World Turned Upside Down

Words & Music by Guy Berryman, Chris Martin, Jon Buckland & Will Champion

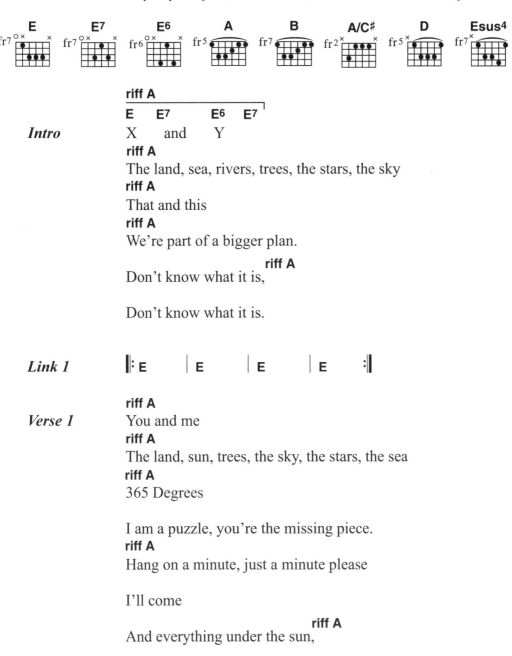

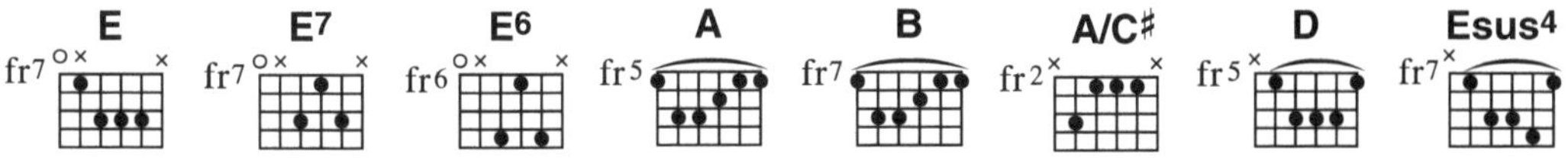

riff A
E E7 E6 E7

Intro
X and Y
riff A
The land, sea, rivers, trees, the stars, the sky
riff A
That and this
riff A
We're part of a bigger plan.
riff A
Don't know what it is,

Don't know what it is.

Link 1 |: E | E | E | E :|

riff A
Verse 1
You and me
riff A
The land, sun, trees, the sky, the stars, the sea
riff A
365 Degrees

I am a puzzle, you're the missing piece.
riff A
Hang on a minute, just a minute please

I'll come
riff A
And everything under the sun,

And everything under the sun.

Chorus 1

A B
What is this feeling that I can't explain
A/C# D
And why am I never gonna sleep again.
A B
What is this thing I've never seen before
A/C# D
A little boy lost in a breaking storm.
A B
Hide and sob, and away they fly
A/C# D
To write your name in the summer sky.
A B
Life has really only just begun
A/C#
Life that comes
D*
And everything under the sun.

Link 2

𝄆 E | E | E | E 𝄇

Verse 2

riff A
X is Y
riff A
The land, sea, rivers, trees, the stars, the sky
riff A
365 Degrees

All of the surface and the underneath.
riff A
Searching your mellow and outsings your key, ah

riff A
And everything under the sun,

And everything under the sun.

Chorus 2

```
A                                          B
What is this feeling that I can't explain
     A/C#                        D
And why am I never gonna sleep again
A                                            B
   What is this thing I've never seen before
  A/C#                D
A little boy lost in a breaking storm
A                                 B
Hide and sob, and away they fly
   A/C#                          D
To write your name in the summer sky
A                                   B
   Life has really only just begun
A/C#
Life that comes
     D*
And everything under the sun
```

Link 3

𝄆 N.C. | N.C. | N.C. | N.C. 𝄇

Bridge

```
B                                            Esus4 E
   And you don't know that you've been born
B                                Esus4 E
   Can't see the calm until the storm
B                                         Esus4 E
   Can't tell your right side from your wrong
B                                    Esus4 E
   Can't see the wave you're riding on.
```

Outro

𝄆 E | E | E | E 𝄇

X&Y

Words & Music by Guy Berryman, Chris Martin, Jon Buckland & Will Champion

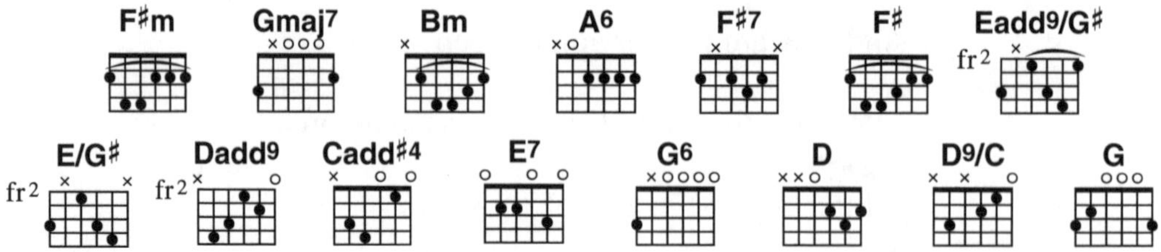

Verse 1

```
F♯m                 Gmaj7
Trying hard to speak and
Bm                    A6
Fighting with my weak hand.
F♯m                 Gmaj7
Driven to dis - traction
    Bm                A6
It's all part of the plan.
F♯7                      Gmaj7
When something is broken
Bm                   A6
And you try and fix it,
F♯m                Gmaj7
Trying to re - pair it
Eadd9/G♯           Gmaj7
Any way you can.
```

Instrumental 1 | Eadd9/G♯ | Gmaj7 | Eadd9/G♯ | Gmaj7 ||

Verse 2

```
  F♯m               Gmaj7
I dive in at the deep end,
Bm                  A6
You become my best friend.
F♯m        Gmaj7            Bm               A6
I want to love you but I don't know if I can,
F♯7                         Gmaj7
I know something is broken
Bm                     A6
And I'm trying to fix it.
```

cont.

F♯m Gmaj7
Trying to re - pair it
Bm A6
Any way I can.

Pre-chorus 1

E/G♯ Gmaj7
Ooh,———
E/G♯ Gmaj7
Ooh,———
E/G♯ Gmaj7
Ooh,———
E/G♯ Gmaj7
Ooh.———

Chorus 1

Dadd9 Cadd♯4 E7
You and me are floating on a tidal wave together,
Dadd9 Cadd♯4 E7
You and me are drifting into outer space and singing:
G6 E/G♯
Ooh,———
G6 E/G♯
Ooh.———

Instrumental 2 ‖: F♯m Gmaj7 | Bm A6 | F♯m Gmaj7 | Bm A6 :‖

Chorus 2

Dadd9 Cadd♯4 E7
You and me are floating on a tidal wave together,
Dadd9 Cadd♯4 E7
You and me are drifting into outer space,
Dadd9 Cadd♯4 E7
You and me are floating on a tidal wave together,
Dadd9 Cadd♯4 E7
You and me are drifting into outer space and singing:
G6 E/G♯
Ooh,———
G6 E/G♯
Ooh,———
G6 E/G♯
Ooh,———
G6 E/G♯
Ooh.———

Outro ‖: D | D9/C | E7 | E7 :‖

‖: G | E/G♯ :‖ *Repeat to fade*

Yellow

Words & Music by Guy Berryman, Chris Martin, Jon Buckland & Will Champion

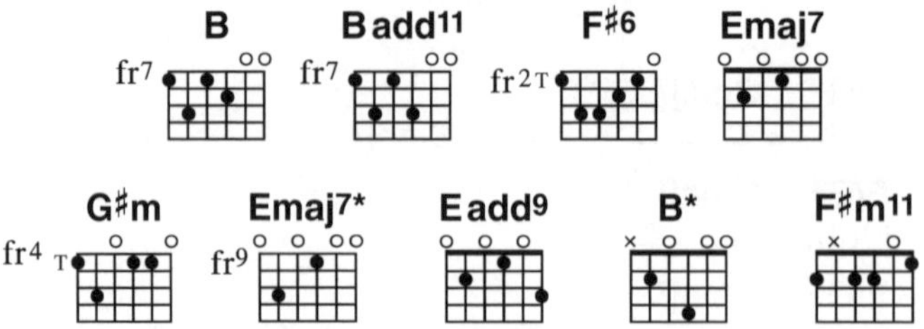

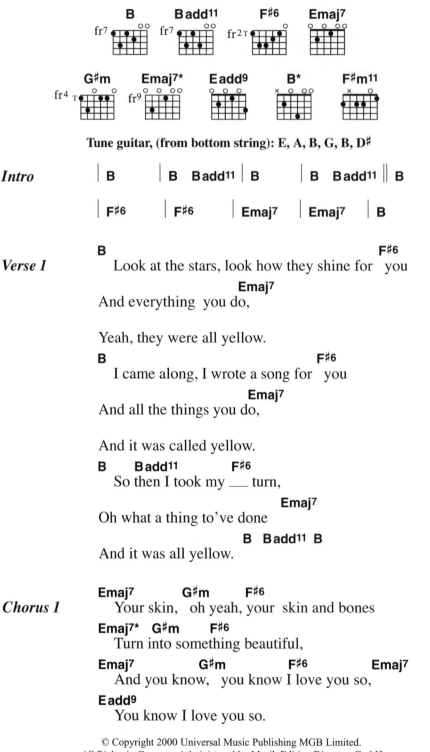

Tune guitar, (from bottom string): E, A, B, G, B, D♯

```
Intro     | B          | B   Badd11 | B          | B   Badd11 || B          | B add11
          | F♯6        | F♯6        | Emaj7      | Emaj7      | B          | B add11 |
```

Verse 1

```
B                                         F♯6
   Look at the stars, look how they shine for   you
                          Emaj7
And everything  you do,

Yeah, they were all yellow.
B                                  F♯6
   I came along, I wrote a song for   you
                            Emaj7
And all the things you do,

And it was called yellow.
B      Badd11         F♯6
   So then I took my ___ turn,
                                Emaj7
Oh what a thing to've done
                           B   Badd11  B
And it was all yellow.
```

Chorus 1

```
Emaj7          G♯m          F♯6
   Your skin,   oh yeah, your  skin and bones
Emaj7*   G♯m       F♯6
   Turn into something beautiful,
Emaj7              G♯m          F♯6              Emaj7
   And you know,    you know I love you so,
Eadd9
   You know I love you so.
```

Link 1

| B | B | F♯6 | F♯6 |
| Emaj7 | Emaj7 | B | B ||

Verse 2

```
B                                        F♯6
   I swam across, I jumped across for   you,
                              Emaj7
Oh, what a thing to do

'Cause you were all yellow.
B                 Badd11         F♯6
   I drew a line, I drew a line for   you,
                          Emaj7
Oh, what a thing to do
                              B   Badd11   B
And it was all yellow.
```

Chorus 2

```
Emaj7       G♯m                F♯6
   Your skin,   oh yeah, your skin and bones
Emaj7*    G♯m       F♯6
   Turn into something beautiful,
Emaj7             G♯m        F♯6             Emaj7
   And you know?   For you I bleed myself dry,
Eadd9
     For you I bleed myself (dry.)
```

Link 2

| B | B | F♯6 | F♯6 |
dry.

| Emaj7 | Emaj7 | B | B ||

Coda

```
    B                                      F♯6
It's true,  look how they shine for you,
                               Emaj7
Look how they shine for you, look how they shine for,
B                                 F♯6
   Look how they shine for you,
                               Emaj7
Look how they shine for you, look how they shine.
B*
   Look at the stars,
                               F♯madd11
Look how they shine for   you
                                  Emaj7
 And all the things that you __ do.
```

Yes

Words & Music by Guy Berryman, Chris Martin, Jon Buckland & Will Champion

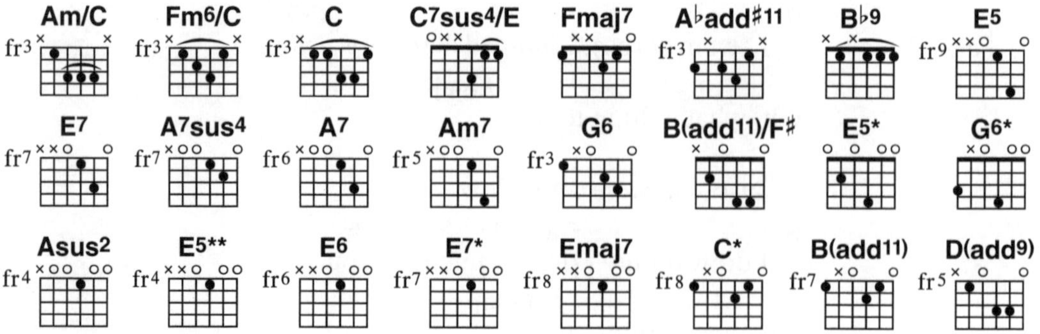

Tune guitar (from bottom string): E, A, E, G, B, E

Intro	Am/C	Fm6/C	C	C7sus4/E
	Fmaj7	A♭add♯11 B♭9	C	N.C.
	𝄆 E5 E7	E5 E7	A7sus4	A7
	Am7 G6	G6	G6	B(add11)/F♯ 𝄇

Verse 1

```
E5  E7                       A7sus4  A7
       When it started we had high    hopes,
          Am7           G6
Now my back's on the line,
                         B(add11)/F♯
My back's on the ropes.
E5  E7                          A7sus4  A7
       When it started we were all       right
     Am7              G6                      B(add11)/F♯
But night makes a fool of us in the day - light.
```

Interlude 1

| E5 E7 | E5 E7 | A7sus4 | A7 |
| Am7 G6 | G6 | G6 | B(add11)/F♯ |

Verse 2

E5 E7 E5 E7 A7sus4 A7
Yeah, we were dy - ing of fru - stra - tion,
Am7 G6 B(add11)/F♯
Saying "Lord lead me not into tempta - tion".
E5 E7 A7sus4 A7 Am7 G6
But it's not easy when she turns you on,
B(add11)/F♯
Sin, stay gone.

Interlude 2

|: E5* | E5* | E5* | E5* :|

Chorus 1

(E5*) G6* Asus2 E5*
If you'd only, if you'd only say yes,
E5** E6 E7* E6 E7* Emaj7
Whether you will's any - bo - dy's guess.
E5* G6* Asus2 E5*
God, only God knows I'm trying my best,
C* B(add11)
But I'm just so tired of this loneliness.

Interlude 3

|: E5 E7 | E5 E7 | A7sus4 | A7 |
| Am7 G6 | G6 | G6 | B(add11)/F♯ :|

Verse 3

E5 E7 E5 E7 A7sus4 A7
So up the picked me by the big toe,
Am7 G6 B(add11)/F♯
I was held from the rooftop then they let go.
E5 E7 E5 E7 A7sus4 A7 Am7 G6
Dizzily scream - ing, "Let the win - dows down!"
B(add11)/F♯ E5*
As I crawl to the ground.

Interlude 4 ‖: E5* | E5* | E5* | E5* :‖

Chorus 2

```
(E5*)       G6*              Asus2    E5*
   If you'd only if you'd only say yes,
E5**         E6   E7*          E6   E7*  Emaj7
   Whether you will's any - bo - dy's guess.
E5*           G6*              Asus2        E5*
   God, only God knows she won't let me rest,
         C*                         B(add11)
But I'm just tired of this lone - liness.
          C*                      B(add11)   D(add9)
I've be - come so tired of this loneli   -   ness.
```

Outro

E5*	G6*	Asus2	E5*
E5** E6	E7* E6	E6 E7* E6	Emaj7
E5*	G6*	Asus2	E5*
C*	C*	B(add11)	B(add11)
E5* ‖

1 2 3 4 5 6 7 8 9